Collin

D0541462

DINOSAURS

ADAM YATES

ILLUSTRATED BY
JON HUGHES

Collins

Reprinted in 2013 for
Independent Book Sales

HarperCollins Publishers Ltd.
77-85 Fulham Palace Road
London W6 8JB

Collins is a registered trademark of
HarperCollins Publishers Ltd.

15 14 13
11 10 9 8 7 6 5 4

Written by Adam Yates
Illustrated by Jon Hughes

First published in 2002 as *Collins Wild Guide Dinosaurs*

© HarperCollins Publishers Ltd, 2002
Illustrations © Jon Hughes, 2002

ISBN: 978 0 00 784143 1

Collins uses papers that are natural, renewable and recyclable
products made from wood grown in sustainable forests. The
manufacturing processes conform to the environmental
regulations of the country of origin.

Printed and bound in China by South China Printing Company

HOW TO USE THIS BOOK

This book covers 120 genera of dinosaurs and other prehistoric animals that lived alongside them (a genus encompasses a group of closely related species). They are grouped into three sections each covering animals from a different period of the Mesozoic Era. Within each period the animals are organised according to the evolutionary relationships.

A symbol corresponding to those on the diagrams in this section, depict each major group. They are presented in the top left-hand corner of each account so you may see at a glance which group each animal belongs to. You can also see quickly which period each animal comes from by looking at the colour of this symbol (Yellow = Triassic, Green = Jurassic, Purple = Cretaceous).

To show exactly when each creature lived a time-wheel is given. Each one starts at the beginning of the Triassic 12 o'clock position and moves clockwise around the circle until it finishes with the end of the Cretaceous at the 12 o'clock position. The sector that is filled in red represents the time span in which that particular animal existed.

A 'fact file' on each animal will give you basic information at a glance. The classification gives you the list of evolutionary groups or 'clades' that the animal belongs to starting with the largest clade (Saurischia or Ornithichia for dinosaurs) and ending with the smallest non-family clade. A family is a clade of closely-related genera. The family name is given at the top of each account above the name of each animal (which appears in large type).

WHAT IS A DINOSAUR?

To many people a dinosaur is any large extinct animal, but to palaeontologists (scientists who specialise in studying prehistoric life) the name has a more precise meaning. Many animals that are commonly thought to be dinosaurs, such as flying pterosaurs and swimming plesiosaurs, are not proper dinosaurs, while many people are unaware that modern birds are actually a surviving part of the dinosaur clan. The modern concept of the group Dinosauria is that it is a 'real' branch of the reptile family tree. It is 'real' in the sense that all dinosaurs are more closely related to one another, than they are to any other reptile group. In other words they are all descended from a single ancestral species: the first dinosaur. All descendants of this common ancestor are included in the Dinosauria, no matter how much they have changed during the course of their evolution. Such evolutionary groups, which include all descendants of a common ancestor, are called 'clades' and it is a requirement of modern classifications of living things that all groups be clades. How does one identify an animal as a member of the clade Dinosauria? We look to the evolutionary novelties, or 'derived characteristics' that the animal displays. We can assume that the ancestor of a clade had evolved some characteristics that were new to it and that its subsequent descendants inherited these derived characteristics (although it is possible for them to be erased or modified by subsequent evolution). In the case of dinosaurs there are a host of rather technical features, four of the most significant are listed below.

i). Special pairs of crests on the top of each neck vertebra that are used for the attachments of tendons to hold the neck in shape.

ii). A first finger, or thumb, that moves in a different direction to the other fingers, so when it is flexed it moves across the palm and when it is extended it points away from the other fingers. This allows the hand to grasp when the thumb is flexed and also allows the large thumb claw to be used as a weapon when the thumb is extended.

iii). An asymmetrical hand with very small fourth and fifth fingers (the 'ring' and 'little' fingers, respectively).

iv). An interlocking and immobile joint between the main bone of the ankle and the larger of the two lower leg bones, making a stiffer, hinge-like ankle that can only bend in one direction of movement.

THE DINOSAURS' PLACE IN THE TREE OF LIFE

Due to the ever-branching nature of evolution, all clades (except the clade of all life) are nested inside larger clades, rather like Russian dolls. Dinosaurs are one clade amongst many (including our own) that are included in the great clade Vertebrata (animals with a backbone). Amongst the vertebrates they belong to the clade Tetrapoda (four-footed, mostly terrestrial vertebrates). Most animals figured in this book are tetrapods (the exception is *Hybodus*, a cartilaginous fish). Within the Tetrapoda, dinosaurs belong to the clade Amniota, which all share the derived character of an egg that contains a membrane surrounding the developing embryo.

The other tetrapod clade is the Amphibia, which have naked jelly-like eggs that are usually laid in water. The Amniota contains two large clades, the Synapsida and the Reptilia.

The Synapsida, which includes modern mammals, share the derived character of a single large hole in the skull for the attachment of jaw muscles. More advanced synapsids, of the Therapsida, also developed differentiated teeth (eg. incisors, canines and molars) and a faster, 'warm-blooded' metabolism.

The Reptilia share such derived characters as a dry scaly skin, and excretion that involves uric acid (this reduces water loss during urination). Thus they well adapted for coping with hot, dry conditions.

Within the reptiles the largest clade is the Diapsida, which have two holes in the temporal region of their skull. Turtles are the only living reptiles that are not diapsids. The three main diapsid clades featured in this book are the Ichthyosauria, the Plesiosauria and the Archosauria. Ichthyosaurs are superficially fish-like marine reptiles whose relationships to other diapsids are uncertain. Plesiosaurians are also marine reptiles that have lost the lower of the two temporal holes in the skull. They are more closely related to modern snakes and lizards than they are to Archosaurs.

The last clade, Archosauria or 'ruling reptiles', contains crocodiles, pterosaurs (flying reptiles), dinosaurs and birds (feathery flying reptiles). Archosaurs share the derived character of a large hole on each side of the skull, in front of each eye and teeth that are set in sockets. Within the Archosauria those that are more closely related to Crocodiles than to dinosaurs form a clade called Crurotarsi. Crurotarsans share an advanced swivel joint between the bones of the ankle.

Pterosaurs are more closely related to dinosaurs than to crocodiles so they are placed in a clade called Ornithodira. All these relationships can be summed up in the following diagram of relationships, known as a cladogram.

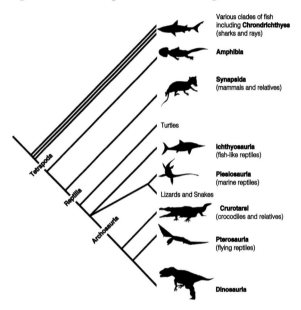

THE MAIN GROUPS OF DINOSAURS

All dinosaurs belong to one of two large clades, the Ornithischia ('Bird Hips') and the Saurischia ('Lizard Hips'). Ornithischians share two main derived characters: a bird-hipped pelvis and a toothless bone (called a predentary) in front of the lower jaws. The bird-hipped condition refers to the fact that the left and right pubis bones (bones in the front of the pelvis) have separated from each other and are rotated backwards to lie parallel to the ischia (bones from the back of the pelvis). This allowed the guts to move back under the hind legs so that they could become longer and heavier without making the animal front-heavy.

The predentary bone provided a stable, single-piece platform to support a horny beak. Both features are adaptations to a diet of plants and all ornithischians were herbivores. The two main clades within Ornithischia were the Thyreophora ('shield bearers') and the Neornithischia ('new bird hips').

Thyreophorans were heavy-bodied quadrupeds that were armoured with bony plates set into their skin. The group includes Stegosauria ('roofed lizards') that had a double row of very tall plates and spikes either side of the midline and Ankylosauria ('fused lizards') that were squat, heavily armoured forms with armour plating on their skulls.

Neornithischia shared the derived characters of a toothless gap in front of the main row of cheek teeth, and teeth that had a thicker layer of enamel on one side (so that a cutting edge was formed when the teeth were worn). Neornithischia itself is comprised of two large clades, the Marginocephalia and the Ornithopoda. Marginocephalians include the horned dinosaurs and the dome-headed dinosaurs. They were a diverse group that are united by a shelf of bone at the back of their heads. Ornithopods were a group of mostly bipedal herbivores that evolved some quadrupedal forms late in the Cretaceous period (see below).

Saurischians, for the most part retain the primitive condition of having a pubic bone that pointed forwards ('lizard-hipped' condition) but share some advanced features, such as an elongated neck and extra joints between the vertebrae of the back (thus stiffening the trunk), that identify the group as a clade. Saurischia is made up of two clades containing rather different looking animals. One clade, the Sauropodomorpha, primarily consists of large, quadrupedal herbivores, whereas the other clade, the Theropoda, are entirely bipedal and are mostly carnivorous. Two groups are recognised within the Sauropodomorpha although one might not be a clade.

The Sauropoda are definitely a clade and all share a gigantic body size, columnar, elephantine legs and a tiny head. The

Prosauropoda include smaller, less specialised forms that may, or may not, be ancestral to the true sauropods.

Theropods are a clade that share a wishbone in the shoulder girdle, and an extra joint in the middle of their lower jaws that allowed their jaws to clamp around struggling prey. The two main theropod clades are the Ceratosauria and Tetanurae. Ceratosaurs flourished early in the history of the dinosaurs but some survived until the end of the Cretaceous. Ceratosaurs share the derived characteristic of fusing up many of the bones in their hips and feet. Tetanurans have a stiff tip to their tails and have only three fingers on each hand. Most tetanurans fall into one of two clades: the Carnosauria or the Coelurosauria.

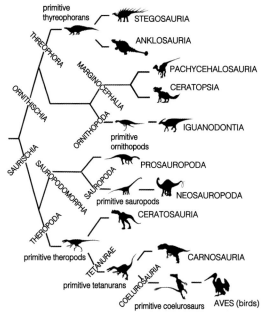

Carnosaurs were large fierce predators with large heads and small arms. They share special pneumatic holes in the bones of the snout which identifies the group as a clade. Coelurosaurs on the other hand were small lightly built animals with small heads and long arms (although exceptions, such as tyrannosaurids did evolve). Advanced coelurosaurs share a number of characteristics with birds such as a large half-moon shaped bone in the wrist and a pubic bone that is bent backwards (as in ornithischians) that show that birds are a part of this clade. A number of coelurosaurian groups abandoned the predatory way of life and evolved into herbivores.

WHEN DINOSAURS LIVED

To discuss the Earth's immensely long history geologists divide the past up into large chunks of time called 'eras'. These Eras are subdivided into smaller lengths called 'periods'. The Era that concerns us is the Mesozoic Era (245–65 million years ago). It is subdivided into three periods, the Triassic (245–208 million years ago), Jurassic (208–146 million years ago) and Cretaceous (146–65 million years ago).

The earliest known dinosaurs are about 230 million years old (from the Late Triassic Period). At that time there were only a few rare species. Synapsids and different groups of reptiles dominated the land. Nevertheless by the end of the Triassic (210 million years ago) almost all medium to large sized land animals were dinosaurs. This dominance continued until the end of the Mesozoic Era (at the end of the Cretaceous Period, 65 million years ago). At this boundary nearly all groups of dinosaur went extinct but one small group of coelurosaurian theropods, the birds, did survive.

'WARM-BLOODED' OR 'COLD-BLOODED' DINOSAURS?

Modern reptiles have a physiology that is commonly referred to as 'cold-blooded'. This is a poor term to use as it is both inaccurate (the body temperature of reptiles can be as high, or higher, than a similar-sized 'warm-blooded' animal) and confuses more than one characteristic. Firstly, animals can be either endothermic or ectothermic. Endotherms generate their own heat internally (by 'burning' more food) while ectotherms rely on the sun to warm them up. Secondly, animals can be either homeothermic or poikilothermic.

Homeotherms have a constant body temperature whereas the body temperature of poikilotherms varies widely. Modern reptiles, except birds, ('cold-bloods') are mostly ectothermic and poikilothermic, but some are ectothermic homeotherms. Modern birds and mammals ('warm-bloods') are mostly endothermic and homeothermic but some are endothermic poikilotherms. Reptiles, except birds, are more efficient than birds and mammals, as they need less food to live, but they become inactive when it is cold. Birds and mammals are, on the other hand, always ready for action, which is just as well because they have a metabolic furnace that needs constant fuelling.

The debate over which strategy the non-birdy dinosaurs used has gone on for more than two decades and is still not resolved. Most agree that dinosaurs were active for most of their lives and maintained a high degree of homeothermy but many do not believe they achieved this by being endothermic.

FURTHER READING

There are a great many books dealing with the subject of dinosaurs and prehistoric life, some much better than others. Here is a brief (and by no means complete) list of the better titles.

Benton, M. J. 2000, *Vertebrate Palaeontology* (2nd edition). Blackwell Scientific, Oxford. The standard vertebrate palaeontology textbook. A good introduction to the broader aspects of prehistoric vertebrate life.

Currie, P. J. and Padian, K. (Eds) 1997. *Encyclopaedia of Dinosaurs*. Academic Press, San Diego. A collection of articles by leading experts, arranged alphabetically. A large authoritative and comprehensive work but the level of detail in the coverage is patchy.

Dingus, L. and Rowe, T. 1998. *The Mistaken Extinction: Dinosaur Evolution and the Origin of Birds*. W. H. Freeman and Co., New York. An excellent introductory text into the modern methods of determining evolutionary relationships and biological classification. The best popular account of why birds should be classified as dinosaurs and an up-to-date account of dinosaur extinction.

Farlow, J. O. and Brett-Surman, M. K. (Eds) 1998. *The Complete Dinosaur*. Indiana University Press, Bloomington. A collection of articles by leading experts covering all aspects of dinosaur biology and evolution. One of the best all-round books for the dinosaur enthusiast.

Fatstovsky, D. E. and Weishampel, D. B. 1996. *The Evolution and Extinction of the Dinosaurs*. Cambridge University Press, Cambridge. The best dinosaur textbook.

Glut, D. 1997. *Dinosaurs: The Encyclopaedia*. McFarland and Co. Inc., Jefferson. A compendium of all the dinosaur genera that were known at the time of printing. Since the rate of discovery of new dinosaurs is so great, two supplementary volumes have been published since the original with more planned for the future. The only easily accessible place to find simple accounts and illustrations of the more obscure dinosaur genera.

Norman, D. B. 1985. *The Illustrated Encyclopaedia of Dinosaurs*. Salamander, London. The classic popular dinosaur book. Beautifully illustrated but unfortunately it is a little out of date now.

Weishampel, D. B., Dodson, P. and Osmólska, H. (Eds) 1990. *The Dinosauria*. University of California Press, Berkeley. The 'bible' for serious dinosaur students. It is a technical account of the anatomy and classification of the major dinosaur groups with smaller sections on other aspects of dinosaur biology.

Wellnhofer, P. 1991. *The Illustrated Encyclopaedia of Pterosaurs*. Salamander, London. A companion volume to Norman's book. The only popular book devoted to pterosaurs, this is also lavishly illustrated.

ID FACT FILE

LENGTH:
2.5 m (8 ft)

WEIGHT:
25 kg (55lb)

TIME:
Late Triassic

CLASSIFICATION:
Saurischia,
Sauropodomorpha,
Prosauropoda

DESCRIPTION:
Small, lightly
built biped, with
some ability to
walk on all fours.
Head small and
neck short
(compared to other
prosauropods).

DIET:
Probably
omnivorous,
soft plants and
small animals.

Thecodontosaurus
(socket-toothed lizard)

This was the first prosauropod dinosaur
to be discovered. Its bones were found in
sediments that fill ancient caves that
were once a part of small, arid, islands in
a shallow sea, in what is now south-west
England.

Thecodontosaurus is also one of the most
primitive of known prosauropods. Unlike
its relatives, it was small and lightly built
and could probably progress comfortably
on two legs for much of the time.

□ Triassic
248–206 million yrs.

■ Jurassic
206–144 million yrs.

■ Cretaceous
144–65 million yrs.

FAMILY THECODONTOSAURIDAE (PROSAUROPODA)

It was not adapted for chewing a large amount plant material, but neither was it fully adapted for life as a carnivore. Its teeth resembled those of a modern iguana in being leaf-shaped and coarsely serrated. This suggests that *Thecodontosaurus*, like the iguana, did include some plant material in its diet. In all probability it was an omnivore, eating both plants and small animals. Its thumb bore a defensive claw that was smaller than that of other prosauropods.

Unfortunately many of the best *Thecodontosaurus* fossils were destroyed during World War II. However, since then bones have been found at a number of sites, which has allowed research to continue.

ID FACT FILE

LENGTH:
9 m (30ft)

WEIGHT:
3 tons

TIME:
Late Triassic

CLASSIFICATION:
Saurischia,
Sauropodomorpha,
Prosauropoda

DESCRIPTION:
Moderately large,
heavy bodied
quadruped with
short forelegs.
Head small, with a
pointed snout,
placed on a
moderately long
neck.

DIET:
Herbivorous

Riojasaurus
(lizard from La Rioja)

Riojasaurus is a South American example of the melanorosaurid family. These were large, robust prosauropods that some scientists think may have been closely related to the ancestors of the gigantic sauropod dinosaurs. Other melanorosaurids have been found in Europe and South Africa.

Riojasaurus had a long pointed snout, which may have been tipped with a small horny beak that would have helped it crop vegetation.

◻ Triassic
248–206 million yrs.

◼ Jurassic
206–144 million yrs.

◼ Cretaceous
144–65 million yrs.

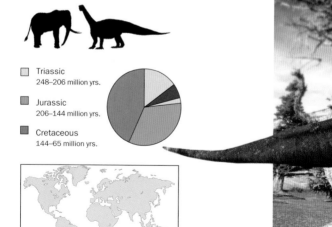

FAMILY MELANOROSAURIDAE (PROSAUROPODA)

Its neck was long but it was still quite stout when compared to other prosauropods such as *Plateosaurus* (see pp. 16–17). Like other prosauropods it had a grasping, five-fingered hand and a four-toed foot. The hands would have been used when the animal reared up to feed on high branches. Its thumb was tipped with a large, curved claw that was used as a weapon. Because its body was so long and heavy it would have had to walk upon all four limbs.

ID FACT FILE

LENGTH:
7.5 m (24½ ft)

WEIGHT:
1.5 tons

TIME:
Late Triassic

CLASSIFICATION:
Saurischia,
Sauropodomorpha,
Prosauropoda

DESCRIPTION:
Moderately large,
heavy bodied
quadruped with
short forelegs.
Head small, with
a deep snout, on
a long neck.

DIET:
Herbivorous

Plateosaurus
(flat lizard)

Plateosaurus was a typical prosauropod. It was also one of the commonest Triassic dinosaurs, and is known from dozens of sites across Europe. It has even been found as far away as Greenland. It is probable that so many skeletons are found because of the seasonally dry climate in which the animal lived.

During times of drought, many *Plateosaurus* became caught, and died, in the deep mud

☐ Triassic
248–206 million yrs.

☐ Jurassic
206–144 million yrs.

☐ Cretaceous
144–65 million yrs.

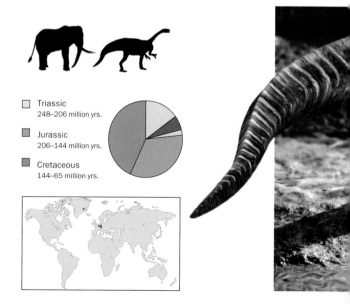

FAMILY PLATEOSAURIDAE (PROSAUROPODA)

surrounding its waterholes. These skeletons would later be buried by sand brought by floodwaters when the drought broke.

Like most saurapodomorphs, *Plateosaurus* had a very large nasal chamber. The reason for this big nose is not known; it may have improved its sense of smell, or helped warm the air it breathed in. *Plateosaurus* differs from more primitive prosauropods by having jaws that were better designed to cope with chewing plants and by having a longer, thinner neck. It also had a strong 'twist' to its thumb, so that when it was straightened its big claw would point away from the rest of the hand.

FAMILY PLATEOSAURIDAE (PROSAUROPODA)

ID FACT FILE

LENGTH:
20 cm (8 in) (baby)

TIME:
Late Triassic

CLASSIFICATION:
Saurischia,
Sauropodomorpha,
Prosauropoda

DESCRIPTION:
Hatchlings are tiny,
slender-limbed
quadrupeds.
Head short and
deep. Lower jaw
with a distinct
'chin'. Neck short
for a prosauropod.

DIET:
Herbivorous

Mussaurus
(mouse lizard)

Mussaurus is mainly known from tiny
skeletons of baby individuals. Adult
prosauropod bones found nearby indicate
they may have grown to 5m (16 ft) in
length. Several individuals were found
close together, along with an egg that
might belong to *Mussaurus*. Small though
the skeletons were, they could not have
fitted inside the egg. This is important
because it
suggests that
the babies

☐ Triassic
248–206 million yrs.

☐ Jurassic
206–144 million yrs.

☐ Cretaceous
144–65 million yrs.

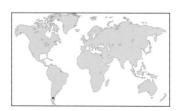

stayed in the nesting area long enough to outgrow their eggs. For this to happen it is necessary for a parent to guard them and provide food. So perhaps *Mussaurus* had parental care, like a modern bird.

The skull of *Mussaurus* has some sauropod-like characteristics, such as a short, high skull and a chin. Does this mean the sauropods evolved their skulls by retaining juvenile features into adulthood, or is it just that *Mussaurus* is especially close to the ancestry of sauropods? Only the study of an adult *Mussaurus* will answer these questions.

ID FACT FILE

LENGTH:
4 m (13 ft)

WEIGHT:
350 kg (770 lb)

TIME:
Late Triassic

CLASSIFICATION:
Saurischia,
Theropoda

DESCRIPTION:
Medium sized,
robust biped.
Head large with
short neck. Four
fingered hands
and four toed feet.

DIET:
Carnivorous,
reptiles including
other dinosaurs.

Herrerasaurus
(Herrera's lizard)

Herrerasaurus is one of the earliest
known dinosaurus and was the largest one
of its time. Scientists are divided in their
opinion of its relationships. Some think it
was a primitive saurischian that was related
to the ancestor of both sauropodomorph
and theropod dinosaurs while others think
it was an early theropod.

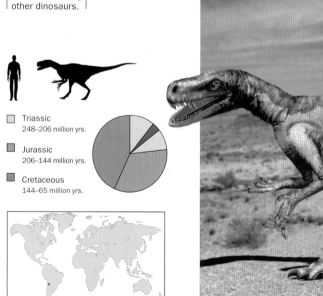

☐ Triassic
248–206 million yrs.

☐ Jurassic
206–144 million yrs.

☐ Cretaceous
144–65 million yrs.

FAMILY HERRERASAURIDAE (THEROPODA)

Like theropods it was a bipedal predator but unlike
all other theropods its first (big) toe was not reduced
and the third (middle) finger was the longest. Its
hands were well adapted for grasping and bore
sharp, curved claws. It also had a large, deep skull
armed with large sharp teeth. The middle teeth of
the upper jaw were especially large and formed
'fangs' that would have stuck out from underneath its
lips. However its legs did not have the proportions
of a fast runner, so it may have ambushed its prey.

FAMILY COELOPHYSIDAE (CERATOSAURIA)

ID FACT FILE

LENGTH:
3 m (10 ft)

WEIGHT:
20 kg (44 lb)

TIME:
Late Triassic

CLASSIFICATION:
Saurischia,
Theropoda,
Ceratosauria

DESCRIPTION:
Small lightly built
biped. Head long
and low on a long,
slender neck.
Hands with four
fingers and feet
with four toes.

DIET:
Carnivorous,
reptiles and
amphibians.

Coelophysis
(hollow form)

Coleophysis was a successful predator of
the Late Triassic. A mass burial of hundreds
of complete skeletons, found at Ghost
Ranch in New Mexico, makes this one of
the best known Triassic dinosaurs. These
dinosaurs probably died together around a
waterhole during a bad drought. The
stomach contents of some of these skeletons
show that *Coleophysis* was not above
eating smaller members of its own
species during times of hardship.

■ Triassic
248–206 million yrs.

■ Jurassic
206–144 million yrs.

■ Cretaceous
144–65 million yrs.

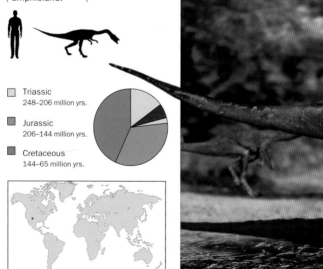

FAMILY COELOPHYSIDAE (CERATOSAURIA)

Coleophysis was more lightly built than the earlier *Herrerasaurus* (see pp. 20–21) so it would have been more nimble. Its foot also differed from that of *Herrerasaurus*, in that the first toe was reduced in size and its bones did not make contact with the ankle. This condition is also found in all later theropod dinosaurs including modern birds. *Coleophysis* and its closest relatives also had a peculiar notch in the upper jaw, just below the nostril. The function of this notch is unknown.

Although quite slender, *Coleophysis* had large, sharp serrated teeth and may have been able to take quite large prey, especially it it hunted in groups.

ID FACT FILE

LENGTH:
5.2 m (17 ft)

TIME:
Late Triassic–
Early Jurassic.

CLASSIFICATION:
Saurischia,
Theropoda,
Ceratosauria

DESCRIPTION:
Medium-sized
lightly built biped.
Like *Coelophysis*
only larger.

DIET:
Carnivorous,
maybe
Plateosaurus.

Liliensternus

(named after Count Von Lilienstern)

This animal was a European relative of *Coelophysis* (see pp. 22–23). The main difference being that it was larger and had fewer vertebrae taking part in the connection between the spine and the hip girdle. Like *Coelophysis* it had a slender build and a distinctive notch in the upper jaw.

For many years the bones of this animal were plastered into the wall of a privately owned castle in Germany. They now

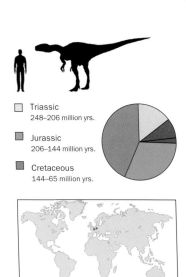

☐ Triassic
248–206 million yrs.

☐ Jurassic
206–144 million yrs.

☐ Cretaceous
144–65 million yrs.

FAMILY COELOPHYSIDAE (CERATOSAURIA)

reside in the Humboldt Museum of Natural History in Germany and can be studied properly. Bones of a second species of *Liliensternus* have been found in France. This species was slightly younger than the original German one and lived during the Early Jurassic. Few other dinosaur genera are known to cross the boundaries of geological periods.

The only known skull is badly broken, so it is not possible to tell whether *Liliensternus* had the twin crests often seen in early ceratosaurs (see *Dilophosaurus*, pp.66–67). *Liliensternus* had quite large teeth and may have hunted *Plateosaurus* (see pp. 16–17), the commonest dinosaur that shared its habitat.

ID FACT FILE

LENGTH:
6 m (20 ft)

TIME:
Late Triassic

CLASSIFICATION:
Reptilia, Diapsida,
Archosauria,
Crurotarsi

DESCRIPTION:
Long, heavy-bodied
quadruped. Skull
large and deep,
with large sharp
teeth. Neck short.
Back and tail
armoured. Five
fingers and toes.

DIET:
Carnivorous,
reptiles and
amphibians.

Postosuchus
(crocodile from Post)

Originally reconstructed as a biped related
to the ancestor of *Tyrannosaurus* (see pp.
196–197), we now know that *Postosuchus*
was a quadruped more closely related to
modern crocodiles than to any dinosaur. It
was a large fierce carnivore that probably
filled the role of top predator in its
environment.

It would be another 150 million years
before any non-dinosaurian land animal
would fill this role. *Postosuchus*, like
dinosaurs, walked erect, with its body

□ Triassic
248–206 million yrs.

■ Jurassic
206–144 million yrs.

■ Cretaceous
144–65 million yrs.

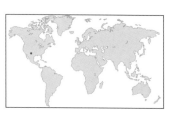

FAMILY RAUISUCHIDAE (CRUROTARSI)

lifted high off the ground and its limbs tucked underneath. This is quite an unusual posture amongst crocodile relatives (a group called the Crurotarsi) which usually have a more sprawling gait.

Like other crurotarsans, including modern crocodiles, *Postosuchus* was lightly armoured with pairs of bony plates that extended along its back and tail. This would have have made it heavy, which means it is likely that *Postosuchus* was an ambush predator rather than a pursuit predator.

The footprints of *Postosuchus* and its relatives have been known for a long time, although at one time they were thought to be made by a giant frog!

ID FACT FILE

LENGTH:
3 m (10 ft)

TIME:
Late Triassic

CLASSIFICATION:
Reptilia, Diapsida, Archosauria, Crurotarsi

DESCRIPTION:
Long, low-slung, heavy bodied quadruped. Head small, ending in little pig-like snout. Heavily armoured over the back and tail. Sides armoured with short spikes. Five toes and fingers.

DIET:
Herbivorous, low growing plants and tubers.

Stagonolepis
(drop scale)

Like *Postosuchus* (see pp. 26–27), *Stagonolepis* was an archosaur related to the ancestors of crocodiles, but it was a very different animal. Its most outstanding feature was its armour which completely covered the back and tail in close fitting rectangular plates. These plates fitted together to form a jointed, flexible carapace.

Along each of its flanks was a row of short, stout spikes. Even the belly and

Triassic
248–206 million yrs.

Jurassic
206–144 million yrs.

Cretaceous
144–65 million yrs.

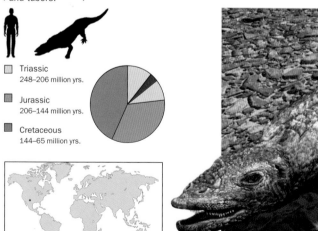

FAMILY STAGONOLEPIDIDAE (CRUROTARSI)

the underside of the tail were covered with bony plates. In other related species, these spikes became long, dangerous prongs that protected the flanks and shoulders. Its skull, with its toothless snout, and small blunt teeth at the rear of the jaws, was also very different from the carnivorous archosaurs. The snout tip was blunt and upturned, looking a little like a pig.

It probably used its snout to grub through soft soil for roots and tubers. The body of *Stagonolepis* was rather narrow from side to side but it had close relatives whose bodies grew very wide and flat. Combined with their armoured carapace these must have looked a lot like turtles.

ID FACT FILE

LENGTH:
3 m (10 ft)

WEIGHT:
1 ton

TIME:
Late Triassic

CLASSIFICATION:
Synapsida,
Therapsida,
Dicynodontia

DESCRIPTION:
Heavy bodied
quadruped with
hippopotamus-
like proportions.
Head very large
and neck short.
Mouth with a horny
beak and two
tusks. Limbs stout
and sprawling.

DIET:
Herbivorous, low
browser.

Placerias

(the pleasing one)

Placerias was one of the last dicynodonts,
a successful group of herbivores that
flourished earlier in the Triassic Period
and in the Permian before that. The
dicynodonts belonged to the Synapsida, a
group of terrestrial vertebrates that includes
mammals and their extinct relatives.

Although frequently called 'mammal-
like-reptiles' this is not strictly true and
Placerias would have lacked such
features as a dry scaly skin and uric

☐ Triassic
248–206 million yrs.

☐ Jurassic
206–144 million yrs.

☐ Cretaceous
144–65 million yrs.

FAMILY KANAMEYERIIDAE (DICYNODONTIA)

acid excretion that identify true reptiles. During their history dicynodonts lost most of their teeth until only two remained. These formed a pair of small tusks in the upper jaw.

Some *Placerias*, perhaps the males, had large bony spikes projecting down and out from the upper jaw. The front of the mouth formed a sharp beak that would have chopped its food into coarse pieces. It then relied on its massive gut, in its barrel-shaped body, to slowly ferment the food. Its limbs were short and squat and would have restricted it to a slow walking gait.

Scelidosaurus

(limb lizard)

ID FACT FILE

LENGTH:
3.5 m (11½ ft)

WEIGHT:
65 kg (143 lb)

TIME:
Early Jurassic

CLASSIFICATION:
Ornithischia,
Thyreophora

DESCRIPTION:
Small, heavy-bodied
quadruped. Head
small and pointed.
Mouth tipped
with a small
horny beak.
Neck, back, flanks
and tail armoured
with longitudinal
rows of bony studs
set in the skin.
Four hind toes,
forefoot unknown.

DIET:
Herbivorous

Scelidosaurus is best known from the
famous cliffs near Lyme Regis in England,
where a number of skeletons have been
found. These were buried in marine
mudstones, suggesting that a river carried
their carcasses out to sea before burial.
Less complete remains are known from
non-marine sediments in North America
and China.

Scelidosaurus was a primitive member of
the Thyreophora, a group of

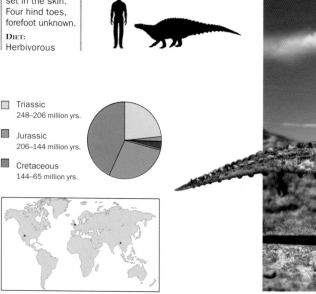

Triassic
248–206 million yrs.

Jurassic
206–144 million yrs.

Cretaceous
144–65 million yrs.

FAMILY SCELIDOSAURIDAE (THYREOPHORA)

armoured ornithischians that includes stegosaurs and ankylosaurs. Although *Scelidosaurus* was not a light biped, like the ancestral ornithischians, it had not developed the short, elephant-like feet of later thyreophorans either.

Its armour consisted of a double row of keeled studs, extending along its neck and back, with four additional rows on each of its flanks. The tail bore an upper and lower row of tall studs and a row of lower studs on each side. There was a unique pair of triple-spiked plates immediately behind the head.

LENGTH:
4 m (13 ft)

WEIGHT:
300 kg (660 lb)

TIME:
Middle Jurassic

CLASSIFICATION:
Ornithischia,
Thyreophora,
Stegosauria

DESCRIPTION:
Medium-sized
heavy bodied
quadruped. Head
small with a blunt
snout. A double
row of tall spike
like plates
extending along
the neck, back and
tail base. Two
pairs of spikes at
the tail tip, and a
large pair over
the shoulders.

DIET:
Herbivorous

Huayangosaurus
(lizard from Huayang)

Huayangosaurus is the most primitive
known stegosaur. Unlike all others the
front of the upper beak bore a row of
small teeth. It also had relatively long
forelimbs so its back would not have
sloped down towards the shoulders as it
did in other stegosaurs. Along its
sides was a single row of small
bony studs rather like those seen
in *Scelidosaurus* (see pp. 32–33).
Like all stegosaurs the double row
of armour along its neck, back and

■ Triassic
248–206 million yrs.

■ Jurassic
206–144 million yrs.

■ Cretaceous
144–65 million yrs.

tail base was enlarged into a series of tall spikes and plates. In *Huayangosaurus* these were all quite narrow and pointed, although they did become broader and more plate-like towards the head.

Like all thyreophorans, it had small teeth with no effective chewing surface. These could only chop its food into coarse pieces, so it must have relied on large guts and high volumes of food to get the nourishment it required.

FAMILY STEGOSAURIDAE (STEGOSAURIA)

ID FACT FILE

LENGTH:
4.5 m (15 ft)

TIME:
Late Jurassic

CLASSIFICATION:
Ornithischia,
Thyreophora,
Stegosauria

DESCRIPTION:
Medium sized
quadruped,
armoured with a
double row of tall
armour plates
that grade into
spikes over the
hips and tail.

DIET:
Herbivorous

Dacentrurus
(very spiky tail)

Dacenturus was the first stegosaur to be discovered. Its skeleton, which was found in 1874, had drifted out to sea before being buried in marine muds. It is distinctive in having forelimbs that are relatively longer than in other stegosaurids, though they were not as long as they were in *Huayangosaurus* (see pp. 34–35). It also had distinctively sharp front and back edges to its tail spines.

☐ Triassic
248–206 million yrs.

☐ Jurassic
206–144 million yrs.

☐ Cretaceous
144–65 million yrs.

FAMILY STEGOSAURIDAE (STEGOSAURIA)

Apart from these features, it was a typical stegosaurid. The back and tail was armoured with a double row of paired plates or spines.

Over the neck and shoulders these were small oval plates, but these get more elongated and spine-like as the row progresses towards the tail so that by the hips, they were long spines. These spines continue along the length of the tail and reached lengths of more than 45 cm (18 in).

ID FACT FILE

LENGTH:
5 m (16½ ft)

WEIGHT:
320 kg (700 lb)

TIME:
Late Jurassic

CLASSIFICATION:
Ornithischia,
Thyreophora,
Stegosauria

DESCRIPTION:
Medium sized
quadruped, with
short forelimbs
and a sloping
back. Armoured
with a double row
of tall armour
plates grading
into spikes over
the hips and tail.
Tail terminates
with a pair of
long spikes. A
pair of spikes over
the shoulders.

DIET:
Herbivorous

Kentrosaurus

(spiked lizard)

Kentrosaurus was a typical stegosaur. It
had paired rectangular plates over the neck
and shoulders that graded into pairs of
sharp spikes over its hips and tail. An extra
pair of spikes also guarded the shoulders.
The forelimbs were particularly short
compared to the hind limbs. This would
have enabled it to browse on ground
covering vegetation but
would have also
reduced the weight
of its front end,
allowing
the animal

☐ Triassic
   248–206 million yrs.

☐ Jurassic
   206–144 million yrs.

☐ Cretaceous
   144–65 million yrs.

FAMILY STEGOSAURIDAE (STEGOSAURIA)

to rear up onto its hind legs to browse on trees. The tall spines of the vertebrae over its back and hips may have provided the necessary leverage to allow its back muscles pull it into the upright position.

Although the skull of *Kentrosaurus* is only known from fragments it was apparently quite like that of *Stegosaurus* which was long and low with a pointed snout and tipped with a toothless beak.

FAMILY STEGOSAURIDAE (STEGOSAURIA)

ID FACT FILE

LENGTH:
9 m (30 ft)

WEIGHT:
2.5 tons

TIME:
Late Jurassic

DESCRIPTION:
Large sized quadruped, with short forelimbs and a sloping back. Head small, beak long and narrow. Two alternating rows of large triangular plates over the back and hips. Tail tipped with two pairs of spikes.

DIET:
Herbivorous

Stegosaurus
(roofed lizard)

By the most famous and well-known stegosaur, *Stegosaurus* is actually quite unusual for the group. It was much larger and lacked the shoulder spines of the other stegosaurs. It also had a basket of little bony studs protecting its throat. Most obvious, however, was the gross enlargement of the dorsal armour into broad triangular plates, which gave the animal its distinctive profile. The arrangement of these plates has been the subject of controversy, but new and complete specimens show that the popular model of

Triassic
248–206 million yrs.

Jurassic
206–144 million yrs.

Cretaceous
144–65 million yrs.

FAMILY STEGOSAURIDAE (STEGOSAURIA)

two alternating rows is correct. The function of these plates has been equally controversial. They could have been radiators for dumping excess heat, but this is unlikely because an insulating horny sheath probably covered them. Perhaps they were simply for display.

Like *Huayangosaurus* (see pp. 34–35), the two pairs of spikes on the end of the tail, when swung from side to side, would have made an effective weapon.

ID FACT FILE

LENGTH:
1 m (3 ft)

WEIGHT:
2 kg (4½ lb)

TIME:
Early Jurassic

CLASSIFICATION:
Ornithischia,
Neornithischia,
Ornithopoda.

DESCRIPTION:
Small-sized, lightly-built quadruped, capable of bipedal locomotion. Head triangular with two pairs of large fangs. Five fingered hand with large thumbclaw. Four toed foot.

DIET:
Herbivorous, ground covering vegetation.

Heterodontosaurus
(different-toothed lizard)

Heterodontosaurus was an unusual little ornithischian. Currently classified as an ornithopod it has a bony lump on each cheek, suggesting that it might be related to pachycephalosaurs and ceratopsians. Behind the typical beak of ornithischians it had a pair of tusk-like teeth in both the upper and lower jaws. These tusks had fine serrations along their edges, which has led one palaeontologist to propose that *Heterodontosaurus* included some meat in its diet. The cheek teeth are very well adapted

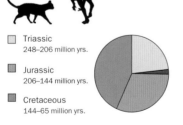

Triassic
248–206 million yrs.

Jurassic
206–144 million yrs.

Cretaceous
144–65 million yrs.

FAMILY HETERODONTOSAURIDAE (ORNITHOPODA)

to chewing plants so this species was unlikely to
have been carnivorous. The tusks were probably
used in display or defence.

Similar skulls have been found that do not have
these tusks, they have been named as a separate
genus, *Abrictosaurus*, but perhaps they are just
female *Heterodontosaurus*. Although lightly built
with short arms, like *Hypsilophodon* (see pp.
148–149), its vertebral column was bent sharply
downwards at the front, which suggests that, for at
least some of the time, it walked on all fours.

FAMILY DRYOSAURIDAE (IGUANODONTIA)

ID FACT FILE

LENGTH:
4 m (13 ft)

WEIGHT:
100 kg (220 lb)

TIME:
Late Jurassic

CLASSIFICATION:
Ornithischia,
Neornithischia,
Ornithopoda,
Iguanodontia

DESCRIPTION:
Medium sized,
lightly-built, long-
legged biped with
a small short skull.
Arms short with
four blunt-clawed
fingers and feet
with three toes.

DIET:
Herbivorous

Dryosaurus
(oak lizard)

Dryosaurus looked very much like a larger version of *Hypsilophodon* (see pp. 148–149) but it possessed numerous specializations seen in more advanced ornithopods, which is why it is classified as an iguanodontian. These specializations include the loss of teeth from the front of the upper jaws, diamond shaped teeth with strong central ridges, and deep grooves on the thigh-bone, just above the knee, for the passage of strong muscles.

Triassic
248–206 million yrs.

Jurassic
206–144 million yrs.

Cretaceous
144–65 million yrs.

FAMILY DRYOSAURIDAE (IGUANODONTIA)

Dryosaurus has been found in both Africa and
North America. The species from these two continents
are almost identical, giving powerful evidence that
there was a continuous connection of land between
them at the time.

The bone microstructure of *Dryosaurus* reveals that
it grew quickly to adulthood without pausing. This
means that either it was 'warm blooded', like a
mammal, or that the climate in which it lived was
equable for the entire year thus allowing such rapid
and continuous growth.

ID FACT FILE

LENGTH:
7 m (23 ft)

WEIGHT:
270 kg (600 lb)

TIME:
Late Jurassic

CLASSIFICATION:
Ornithischia,
Neornithischia,
Ornithopoda,
Iguanodontia

DESCRIPTION:
Medium sized,
heavily built biped
with a long, low,
skull. Hands with
five fingers and
feet with four toes.

DIET:
Herbivorous

Camptosaurus
(bent lizard)

Camptosaurus was another early
iguanodontian, like *Dryosaurus* (see pp.
44–45), but its larger, heavy body and
long snout with close packed teeth were
more like later, advanced, iguanodontians
such as *Iguanodon* (see pp. 156–157).

Nevertheless, *Camptosaurus* retained a
number of primitive features not seen in
more advanced iguanodontians, such as
fewer than 20 rows of teeth in each jaw, a

Triassic
248–206 million yrs.

Jurassic
206–144 million yrs.

Cretaceous
144–65 million yrs.

FAMILY CAMPTOSAURIDAE (IGUANODONTIA)

hand adapted to bearing weight while walking on four legs and a small inner toe (equivalent of our 'big toe'). Its teeth only had a tough enamel layer on one side, which formed a sharp cutting edge.

This feature is also found in later iguanodontians and indicates that they may have been including tougher browse in their diet, with more thorough chewing of their food. With its stockier body, *Camptosaurus* would not have been as swift as its contemporary, *Dryosaurus*.

Massospondylus
(massive spine)

Massospondylus was smaller, but otherwise similar in appearance to, the Triassic *Plateosaurus* (see pp. 16–17). The differences between the two largely lie in details of the skull and teeth. The teeth of *Massospondylus* are peg-shaped and weakly serrated compared to the leaf-shaped, heavily serrated teeth of *Plateosaurus*.

Externally, the main difference would have been that *Massospondylus* had relatively bigger claws on the thumb and big toe.

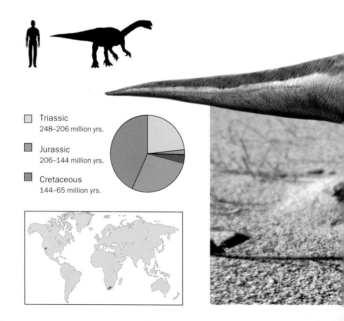

Triassic
248–206 million yrs.

Jurassic
206–144 million yrs.

Cretaceous
144–65 million yrs.

FAMILY MASSOSPONDYLIDAE (PROSAUROPODA)

Massospondylus is interesting because its remains
are commonly found in rocks that were once sand
dunes in a desert. It shared these deserts with close
relatives of *Coelophysis* (see pp. 22–23) which
probably preyed upon it.

Deserts were widespread throughout the world in
the Early Jurassic and *Massospondylus* has been found
in such far flung locations as Southern Africa and
Western North America. Some palaeontologists have
speculated that *Massospondylus* was a carnivore, but
since it was the most common dinosaur in its habitat
this is unlikely – there would not have been enough
prey in these desert areas to support large groups of
Massospondylus.

FAMILY VULCANODONTIDAE (SAUROPODA)

ID FACT FILE

LENGTH:
7 m (23 ft)

TIME:
Early Jurassic

CLASSIFICATION:
Saurischia
Sauropodomorpha
Sauropoda

DESCRIPTION:
Large heavy-bodied quadruped. Limbs columnar. Foot with five toes, the first four with flat claws.

DIET:
Herbivorous

Vulcanodon
(volcano tooth)

Until recently this was the earliest and most primitive of known sauropods, however new discoveries in China and Thailand may take these titles from it. The only known specimen was found sandwiched between lava flows, hence its name, which means 'volcano tooth'. The teeth that were found with the headless skeleton were blade-shaped and belonged to a carnivore. At first scientists thought that *Vulcanodon* may have been a carnivorous sauropod, however, its slow-moving, heavy body was most inappropriate for predation.

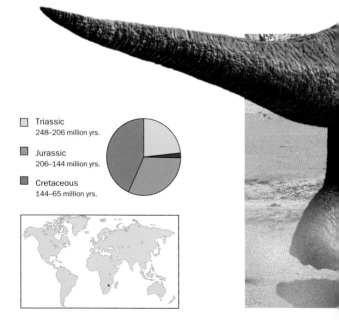

☐ Triassic
248–206 million yrs.

☐ Jurassic
206–144 million yrs.

☐ Cretaceous
144–65 million yrs.

FAMILY VULCANODONTIDAE (SAUROPODA)

All of the teeth lacked roots and probably became mixed with the *Vulcanodon* remains when a carnivorous dinosaur fed on its carcass and shed some teeth. This was not the first time that such an association has fooled palaeontologists.

Vulcanodon shares columnar, elephantine limbs with more advanced sauropods but did not have the short compact foot that these dinosaurs had. Instead the foot of *Vulcanodon* was longer, like that of a prosauropod.

ID FACT FILE

LENGTH:
10 m (33 ft)

WEIGHT:
5 tons

TIME:
Middle Jurassic

CLASSIFICATION:
Saurischi
Sauropodomorpha
Sauropoda

DESCRIPTION:
Large heavy-bodied
quadruped with a
long neck and a
small head.
Hand with five
short fingers,
first with a large
claw. Foot with
five short toes,
first three with
claws. Long tail
ending in a bony
club with three
conical spikes.

DIET:
Herbivorous

Shunosaurus
(lizard from Shuo)

Shunosaurus is one of the few sauropods known from its entire skeleton. Many specimens were unearthed by Chinese palaeontologists working in Dashanpu Quarry in the Sichuan province.

It was a primitive member of a uniquely Chinese family of sauropods, the Euhelopodidae. They were characterized by having greatly elongated necks. The neck of *Shunosaurus* was long (it had an extra vertebra compared to other early sauropods) but it was quite short compared to its advanced relatives such as

☐ Triassic
248–206 million yrs.

☐ Jurassic
206–144 million yrs.

☐ Cretaceous
144–65 million yrs.

Mamenchisaurus (see pp.54–55). The head of *Shunosaurus* was typical for an early sauropod, with broad U-shaper jaws, filled with spoon-shaped teeth and large nostrils placed high up on the snout.

A unique feature of *Shunosaurus* was that its tail ended in a bony club with a row of conical spikes across the top. No other sauropod has such a weapon, which could have been used for defence against predators or territorial battles with other *Shunosaurus*.

Like other sauropods, *Shunosaurus* had a large claw on its thumb, which could have been used for defence, or simply for gripping the ground.

FAMILY EUHELOPODIDAE (SAUROPODA)

ID FACT FILE

LENGTH:
23 m (75 ft)

WEIGHT:
18 tons

TIME:
Late Jurassic

CLASSIFICATION:
Saurischia
Sauropodomorpha
Sauropoda

DESCRIPTION:
Very large
quadruped with
an immensely
long neck and a
tiny head. The
forelimbs were
long and the back
sloped down from
the shoulders to
the hips.

DIET:
Herbivorous

Mamenchisaurus
(lizard from Mamenchi)

Mamenchisaurus was an advanced relative
of *Shunosaurus*. It had carried the neck
elongation trend to its extreme, with seven
extra vertebrae in its neck and the longest
neck known in the animal kingdom
(9.8 m/32 ft). Strangely the neck may not
have been able to be raised up, it instead
gave the animal a greater feeding range
while standing still. Certain details of its
skeleton resemble *Diplodocus* (see pp.
58–59), and its relatives such as split spines
on top of the trunk vertebrae and sled-like

☐ Triassic
248–206 million yrs.

☐ Jurassic
206–144 million yrs.

☐ Cretaceous
144–65 million yrs.

Family Euhelopodidae (Sauropoda)

bones in the tail. So *Mamenchisaurus* was first classified as a diplodocid. However when the skull of *Mamenchisaurus* was finally found it turned out to be almost identical to that of *Shunosaurus* (see pp. 52–53).

We now know that *Mamenchisaurus* is not especially close to diplodocids and that the skeletal similarities between the two are the result of convergent evolution (similar pressures and problems producing similar adaptations in unrelated animals).

FAMILY DIPLODOCIDAE (NEOSAUROPODA)

ID FACT FILE

LENGTH:
21 m (70 ft)

WEIGHT:
22.5 tons

TIME:
Late Jurassic

CLASSIFICATION:
Saurischia
Sauropodomorpha
Sauropoda
Neosauropoda

DESCRIPTION:
Very large heavy-bodied quadruped. Head small with long, low snout. Long, thick neck. Columnar limbs. Back slopes down to the shoulders. Single large claw on forefoot. Hindfoot with three claws. Tail ending in long whip-like tip.

DIET:
Herbivorous

Apatosaurus
(deceptive lizard)

More commonly known in the popular press as *Brontosaurus*, this animal has been dogged by misunderstandings since it was first found in the American Midwest in the 1870s. When reconstructing the skeleton for the first time, its describer Othniel Marsh, used a skull that was found some distance from the original, headless skeleton. The skull closely resembled that of *Camarasaurus* (see pp. 62–63), which was supposed to be a relative.

As our understanding of sauropod anatomy improved this reconstruction became an oddity.

☐ Triassic
248–206 million yrs.

■ Jurassic
206–144 million yrs.

■ Cretaceous
144–65 million yrs.

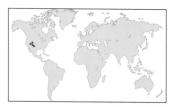

FAMILY DIPLODOCIDAE (NEOSAUROPODA)

Despite its thick limbs and heavy body, *Apatosaurus* shares many features with the light-weight, *Diplodocus* (see pp. 58–59). These include short forelimbs with a back that slopes up from the shoulders to the hips, sled-like bones in the tail, and a long whip-like tip to the tail. The puzzle was solved when the true skull of *Apatosaurus* was identified. It is almost identical to that of *Diplodocus*, and not at all like *Camarasaurus*, resulting in a reclassification of *Apatosaurus*.

ID FACT FILE

LENGTH:
27 m (90 ft)

WEIGHT:
19.5 tons

TIME:
Late Jurassic

CLASSIFICATION:
Saurischia
Sauropodomorpha
Sauropoda
Neosauropoda

DESCRIPTION:
Very large but
slender quadruped.
Head small with
long, low snout.
Long thin neck.
Back and tail
armoured with a
row of conical
spikes. Back
slopes down to the
shoulders. Single
large claw on
forefoot. Hindfoot
with three claws.
Tail ending in long
whip-like tip.

DIET:
Herbivorous

☐ Triassic
   248–206 million yrs.

☐ Jurassic
   206–144 million yrs.

☐ Cretaceous
   144–65 million yrs.

Diplodocus
(double beam)

Diplodocus owes its name to the sled-like bones under each tail vertebrae that formed a double row of 'skids' along the length of the tail. Despite being one of the longest dinosaurs, it was a lightly built for a sauropod and weighed less than its shorter cousin, *Apatosaurus* (see pp.56–57). Its skull is quite modified compared to other sauropods. The teeth are restricted to the tip of the elongate muzzle, where they form a comb-like array of slender peg-shaped teeth.

FAMILY DIPLODOCIDAE (NEOSAUROPODA)

The nostrils are united into a single opening on top of the head between the eyes.

Amongst the distinctive features of *Diplodocus* and its relatives are its particularly short forelimbs. Perhaps this was an adaptation to reducing weight at the front of the animal so that it could rear up and rest upon its tail while feeding at great heights. The 'skids' below the may have protected the nerves and blood-vessels of the tail from being crushed.

ID FACT FILE

LENGTH:
35 m (115 ft)

TIME:
Late Jurassic

CLASSIFICATION:
Saurischia
Sauropodomorpha
Sauropoda
Neosauropoda

DESCRIPTION:
Like Diplodocus
but larger and
with relatively
shorter legs.

DIET:
Herbivorous

Seismosaurus

(earthquake lizard)

Looking like an oversized version of
Diplodocus (indeed one palaeontologist has
suggested that the only known specimen
is merely a large *Diplodocus* (see pp.
58–59), this animal may have been the
longest animal to have ever lived.
However, like *Diplodocus*, it was not
particularly heavily-built. The main
distinguishing feature
between *Seismosaurus* and
other diplodocids is its
relatively short legs. Indeed
it has been described as a
'dinosaurian dachshund'.

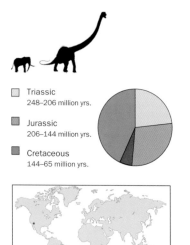

- ☐ Triassic
  248–206 million yrs.

- ☐ Jurassic
  206–144 million yrs.

- ☐ Cretaceous
  144–65 million yrs.

FAMILY DIPLODOCIDAE (NEOSAUROPODA)

Like other diplodocids, *Seismosaurus*, probably had
a neck that could not be elevated from the
shoulders. To browse on tree tops the animal would
have to rear up onto its back legs and tail. Some
palaeontologists doubt that this was possible and
suspect that the long neck improved the reach of a
low browsing animal. This issue remains unresolved.
It also had a long whip like tip to its tail. It is
possible, though not certain, that this could
have been cracked like a whip to deter
predators.

FAMILY CAMARASAURIDAE (NEOSAUROPODA)

ID FACT FILE

LENGTH:
18 m (60 ft)

WEIGHT:
12 tons

TIME:
Late Jurassic

CLASSIFICATION:
Saurischia
Sauropodomorpha
Sauropoda
Neosauropoda

DESCRIPTION:
Large, heavy-bodied
quadruped with
columnar limbs.
Neck long but
relatively shorter
than in other
sauropods. Head
short and box-
shaped. Level
back. Forefoot with
single large claw.
Hindfoot with
three claws.

DIET:
Herbivorous

Camarasaurus

(chambered lizard)

The name of this dinosaur refers to the large cavities that invade the neck and trunk vertebrae and hollowing them out so that they are a light construction of thin bony sheets. Such vertebrae are characteristic of advanced sauropods (neosauropods) and in life were probably filled with a system of air sacs, that grew from outpockets of the lungs. Birds today have similar air sacs and hollowed vertebrae.

Camarasaurus was a medium sized sauropod with a relatively short neck compared to such giants as

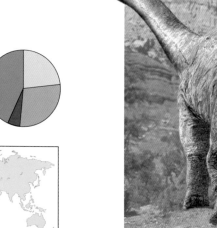

☐ Triassic
   248–206 million yrs.

☐ Jurassic
   206–144 million yrs.

☐ Cretaceous
   144–65 million yrs.

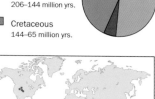

Diplodocus (see pp. 58–59) and *Brachiosaurus* (see pp. 64–65), which shared its habitat. We don't know exactly how the ecology of *Camarasaurus* differed from other sauropods but we know from coarse scratches on its tooth enamel that it did feed on tougher vegetation than *Diplodocus* did. *Camarasaurus* had exceptionally large nasal chambers that were placed high up on its snout which suggests that it was more related to *Brachiosaurus* than to *Diplodocus*.

ID FACT FILE

LENGTH:
21 m (70 ft)

WEIGHT:
28 tons

TIME:
Late Jurassic

CLASSIFICATION:
Saurischia
Sauropodomorpha
Sauropoda
Neosauropoda

DESCRIPTION:
Very large
quadruped. Head
with long, broad
snout. Nose forms
a hump on top of
the head. Very
long forelegs.
Back slopes down
to hips. Forefoot
with single, small
claw. Hindfoot with
three claws. Tail
short relative to
other sauropods.

DIET:
Herbivorous

☐ Triassic
248–206 million yrs.

☐ Jurassic
206–144 million yrs.

☐ Cretaceous
144–65 million yrs.

Brachiosaurus

(arm lizard)

Brachiosaurus is the largest dinosaur for
which we have most of the skeleton.
Larger sauropods, such as
Argentinasaurus did exist, but these are
known from just a few bones.

Brachiosaurus is
remarkable for the
extreme development of
the length of the front
limbs, which exceeded
the length of the
hindlimbs and caused
the back to slope down
to the hips from the
shoulders.

FAMILY BRACHIOSAURIDAE (NEOSAUROPODA)

This obviously raised the base of the neck, which enabled *Brachiosaurus* to browse at higher levels than other contemporary sauropods (except perhaps diplodocids feeding in an upright stance). Despite many restorations to the contrary the vertebrae from the base of the neck suggest that it could not raise its neck into a vertical pose. Like *Camarasaurus* (see pp. 62–63), *Brachiosaurus* had very large nasal chambers that were placed far back on its head. They formed a hump that lay behind its broad muzzle.

Like *Dryosaurus* (see pp. 44–45), *Brachiosaurus* is found in both Africa and North America.

ID FACT FILE

LENGTH:
6 m (20 ft)

WEIGHT:
25 kg (55lb)

TIME:
Early Jurassic

CLASSIFICATION:
Saurischia
Theropoda
Ceratosauria

DESCRIPTION:
Medium-sized,
lightly built biped.
Head long with
two, thin,
semicircular
crests on top.
Neck slender.
Hands with four
fingers and feet
with four toes.
Long flexible tail

DIET:
Carnivorous

Dilophosaurus
(double-crested lizard)

Dilophosaurus is a moderately large
ceratosaur that is quite closely related to the
coelophysid family (see *Coelophysis* pp.
22–23). Like them it had a four-fingered
hand and a curious notch in its upper jaw.
It differed from the coelophysids in being
larger and more heavily built with a
deeper skull.

However the most outstanding
characteristic of *Dilophosaurus* was the
paired, semi-circular
plates that grew on top
of its head.

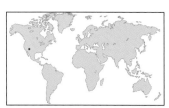

Triassic
248–206 million yrs.

Jurassic
206–144 million yrs.

Cretaceous
144–65 million yrs.

These plates were so thin that they would not have withstood any forceful blows and therefore were almost certainly used as display structures.

The teeth of *Dilophosaurus* were unusual as well, being a lot longer and thinner than the teeth of other predatory dinosaurs. These teeth and the rather weak joint between the tip of the snout and the upper jaws suggest that it did not tackle very large struggling prey. It may have specialized on smaller game such as little reptiles, amphibians and fish.

ID FACT FILE

LENGTH:
6 m (20 ft)

WEIGHT:
450 kg (990 lb)

TIME:
Late Jurassic

CLASSIFICATION:
Saurischia
Theropoda
Ceratosauria

DESCRIPTION:
Medium sized,
heavily built biped.
Neck short and
head large and
deep. Paired
horns in front of
each eye and a
single horn on
top of the snout.
Arms short, hands
with four fingers.
Feet with three
large toes and a
reduced third toe.
Long, deep,
flexible tail.

DIET:
Carnivorous

☐ Triassic
248–206 million yrs.

◼ Jurassic
206–144 million yrs.

◼ Cretaceous
144–65 million yrs.

Ceratosaurus

(horned lizard)

The short powerful neck and large head of
Ceratosaurus gave it the appearance of a
carnosaur. Nevertheless many features of
its skeleton show that it was a more
primitive kind of theropod and that its real
relationships lie with the early *Coelophysis*
(see pp. 22–23) and *Dilophosaurus* (see
pp. 66–67).

These features include a four-fingered
hand and fusion of the
different bones of the hip.
Ceratosaurus had a
distinctive appearance,

FAMILY CERATOSAURIDAE (CERATOSAURIA)

with two short horns in front of each eye and a taller flattened horn on top of the snout, just behind its nostrils. It is also the only theropod known to have had a row of bony armour studs extending along its back.

Ceratosaurus also had a deep muscular tail, that would have been supple all the way to its tip, another feature that sets it apart from the carnosaurs which were tetanuran ('stiff tailed') theropods.

FAMILY UNNAMED (CERATOSAURIA)

ID FACT FILE

LENGTH:
6 m (20 ft)

WEIGHT:
200 kg (440 lb)

TIME:
Late Jurassic

CLASSIFICATION:
Saurischia
Theropoda
Ceratosauria

DESCRIPTION:
Medium sized,
lightly built, long-
bodied biped.
Long, thin neck.
Slender weak
arms with long
thin fingers. Long
legs with three-
toed feet.

DIET:
Probably
carnivorous.

Elaphrosaurus
(light-weight lizard)

It is unfortunate that the only known skeleton of *Elaphrosaurus* is missing the skull. This plus the unusual features of its skeleton make it a difficult theropod to classify. It was once classified as a coelurosaur based upon its slender build. It has even been called a primitive ancestor of the Cretaceous 'ostrich mimic' dinosaurs, such as *Struthiomimus* (see pp. 202–203). We now think that it is a ceratosaur, like *Coelophysis* (see pp. 22–23).

☐ Triassic
248–206 million yrs.

☐ Jurassic
206–144 million yrs.

☐ Cretaceous
144–65 million yrs.

FAMILY UNNAMED (CERATOSAURIA)

Amongst ceratosaurs its straight upper arm bone with reduced muscle attachments, resembles the upper arm bone of the abelisaurid *Carnotaurus* (see pp. 180–181).

It is quite probable that *Elaphrosaurus* was an early relative of the abelisaurids. Although abelisaurids and their relatives are widespread and diverse in the Cretaceous of the Southern Hemisphere no others are known from the Jurassic. Although no skull has been found its is most likely that, like all other ceratosaurs, *Elaphrosaurus* was a carnivore.

FAMILY TORVOSAURIDAE (TETANURAE)

ID FACT FILE

LENGTH:
4.5 m (15 ft)

WEIGHT:
250 kg (550 lb)

TIME:
Middle Jurassic

CLASSIFICATION:
Saurischia
Theropoda
Tetanurae

DESCRIPTION:
Medium sized
biped. Head large
and deep. Neck
short. Arms short.
Thumb with large
claw. Feet with
three four toes.
The first toe is
very reduced.

DIET:
Carnivorous

Eustreptospondylus
(well-twisted spine)

The upper and lower halves of the
vertebrae of the only known skeleton of
Eustreptospondylus have not fused
together suggesting that the individual was
not fully-grown at the time death. It is not
known how much bigger it could have
got. It appears to have been a typical
early tetanuran theropod with a large
deep skull, curved blade-like teeth and
short arms. A number of
features such as the lack
of little horns in front of

☐ Triassic
248–206 million yrs.

☐ Jurassic
206–144 million yrs.

☐ Cretaceous
144–65 million yrs.

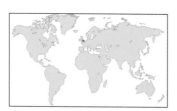

FAMILY TORVOSAURIDAE (TETANURAE)

the eyes and broad pubic bones suggest that it was a
close relative of a particularly large and fearsome
theropod from North America called *Torvosaurus*.
Eustreptospondylus and *Torvosaurus* also share
a large thumb claw and a short forearm with the
bizarre spinosaurids (see *Baryonyx*, pp. 184–185)
suggesting that the two groups might be related.

Eustreptospondylus probably lived on the small
islands that dotted the sea in which it was buried. It
may have been an island hopping beachcomber.

ID FACT FILE

LENGTH:
7 m (23 ft)

TIME:
Middle Jurassic

CLASSIFICATION:
Saurischia
Theropoda
Tetanurae

DESCRIPTION:
Large, heavily-built biped. Head large with many sharp blade-like teeth in the jaws. Arms short but powerful. Feet with three weight supporting toes and a reduced first toe.

DIET:
Carnivorous, other dinosaurs.

Megalosaurus
(big lizard)

Megalosaurus was the first dinosaur to receive a scientific name. It was named by William Buckland, in 1824, and was based on a piece of jaw with large blade-like teeth from Stonesfield, in England. Since it was the first to be named many subsequent discoveries of carnivorous dinosaurs from all around the world were attributed to this genus. However we know that nearly all of these identifications are wrong and that only material from Stonesfield can be properly called *Megalosaurus*.

☐ Triassic
248–206 million yrs.

☐ Jurassic
206–144 million yrs.

■ Cretaceous
144–65 million yrs.

FAMILY MEGALOSAURIDAE (TETANURAE)

Despite having such a long history we still know little about this dinosaur. It was a large carnivorous theropod that would have looked superficially like a carnosaur such as *Allosaurus* (see pp. 80–81).

However, it had certain primitive characteristics of the hip and thigh that indicate that, although it was a tetanuran (stiff-tailed theropods that are more closely related to birds than to ceratosaurs), it was neither a carnosaur, nor a coelurosaur. It might have been a relative of *Eusteptospondylus* (see pp. 72–73).

ID FACT FILE

LENGTH:
5 m (16½ ft)

TIME:
Middle Jurassic

CLASSIFICATION:
Saurischia
Theropoda
Tetanurae
Carnosauria

DESCRIPTION:
Medium sized
biped. Head long
and low (for a
carnosaur). Tall
crest from above
the eyes to the
snout tip. Neck
short. Arms short.

DIET:
Carnivorous,
other dinosaurs.

Monolophosaurus
(single crested lizard)

Monolophosaurus is known from a
beautiful skull and partial skeleton found in
the Gurbantunggut Desert of China. It was
a small carnosaur, possibly belonging to the
allosaurid family. Its most distinctive feature
was a tall crest running along the top of
its skull. CAT scans indicate that this crest
was a delicate hollow structure. It was
probably used for display.

Carnosaurs are
characterized by large
deep and narrow heads
filled with blade-like
teeth mounted short

Triassic
248–206 million yrs.

Jurassic
206–144 million yrs.

Cretaceous
144–65 million yrs.

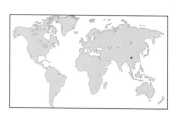

necks, with short but powerful arms. They were
predators that may have killed their prey by
delivering several, quick slashing bites.

Despite their fearsome nature, carnosaurs have certain
bird-like features, including a three fingered hand, a
braced joint between the upper ankle bone and the
main lower leg bone and a tail that was stiff and
inflexible at its tip. These features indicate that
carnosaurs were more closely related to birds
than they were to ceratosaurian theropods.

ID FACT FILE

LENGTH:
8 m (26 ft)

TIME:
Early Jurassic

CLASSIFICATION:
Saurischia
Theropoda
Tetanurae
Carnosauria

DESCRIPTION:
Large biped.
Large, deep
head. Tall,
forward curving,
plate-like crest in
front of eyes.

DIET:
Carnivorous,
prosauropods.

Cryolophosaurus
(frozen-crested lizard)

This is currently the only named dinosaur known from Antarctica. It was found on Mount Kirkpatrick, close to the South Pole. Nevertheless, Antarctica had a more northerly position in the Early Jurassic and the global climate was warmer. Therefore it is unlikely that *Cryolophosaurus* ever had to contend with freezing conditions.

Cryolophosaurus had a large, deep skull, rather like that of *Allosaurus* (see pp. 80–81) but with a most unusual crest.

☐ Triassic
248–206 million yrs.

☐ Jurassic
206–144 million yrs.

■ Cretaceous
144–65 million yrs.

FAMILY ALLOSAURIDAE (CARNOSAURIA)

This crest was a thin, ridged plate that was placed on top of the head, just in front of the eyes. This plate, which curved forward, was unlike most of dinosaur crests in being flattened front-to-back and being broad from sided to side.

Apart from this unusual feature *Cryolophosaurus* was a fairly primitive carnosaur, which is in keeping with it being the earliest known member of the group. Fragmentary remains of prosauropods were found with it and it almost certainly preyed upon these.

FAMILY ALLOSAURIDAE (CARNOSAURIA)

ID FACT FILE

LENGTH:
8 m (26 ft)

WEIGHT:
1 ton

TIME:
Late Jurassic

CLASSIFICATION:
Saurischia
Theropoda
Tetanurae
Carnosauria

DESCRIPTION:
Large, heavily-
built biped. Large,
deep head with
small horns in
front of each eye.
Short, thick neck.
Short, powerful
arms. Three
fingers with large
curved claws.

DIET:
Carnivorous

Allosaurus

(other lizard)

Allosaurus is the commonest large predator of the Late Jurassic. Most remains are from Western North America but have also been found in Portugal. It was a fairly typical carnosaur in outward appearance.

It had a large, deep head on a short powerful neck and short, strong arms tipped with three large claws. Its long

☐ Triassic
248–206 million yrs.

☐ Jurassic
206–144 million yrs.

☐ Cretaceous
144–65 million yrs.

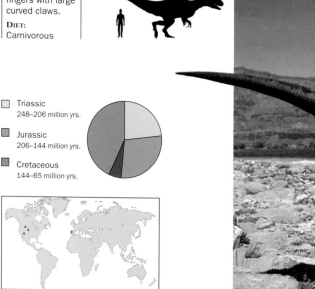

legs were robust and did not have the speedy running proportions of coelurosaurs. The last third of the tail was thin and stiff as is typical of most tetanurans.

Studies of its jaw and skull mechanics indicate that the animal used its upper jaws like a hatchet when attacking its prey. Support for this idea comes from the extremely wide gape that the jaw joint allowed and the shock-absorbing ability of its skull. Its skull was decorated for display with little horns in front of each eye and a ridge on each side of the snout.

ID FACT FILE

LENGTH:
1 m (3 ft)

WEIGHT:
3.5 kg (8 lb)

TIME:
Late Jurassic

CLASSIFICATION:
Saurischia
Theropoda
Tetanurae
Coelurosauria

DESCRIPTION:
Small, lightly built biped. Moderately small head with a pointed snout. Neck long. Arms short. Probably three small fingers. Legs long with three large toes and a reduced first toe. Tail very long with a stiff tip. Covered with 'protofeathers'.

DIET:
Carnivorous, small mammals, lizards

☐ Triassic
248–206 million yrs.

▨ Jurassic
206–144 million yrs.

■ Cretaceous
144–65 million yrs.

Compsognathus

(pretty jaw)

For more than a century *Compsognathus* held the title of the smallest known adult dinosaur. With the inclusion of birds in the Dinosauria, this honour now belongs to the bee hummingbird which is 6.2 cm (2½ in) long. If we exclude birds from consideration the newly discovered *Microraptor* (see pp. 220–221) is now the smallest. *Compsognathus* was an inhabitant of the small desert islands that were also home to *Archaeopteryx* (see pp. 86–87).

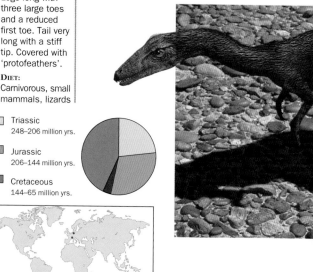

FAMILY COMPSOGNATHIDAE (COELUROSAURIA)

The skeleton of a lizard has been found in the
ribcage of one of the two known *Compsognathus*
skeletons. A closely related genus from China,
Sinosauropteryx, has been found with a small
mammal in its abdominal cavity. These specimens
amply demonstrate that compsognathids were
voracious predators of small terrestrial vertebrates.

Sinosauropteryx also has a coat of unbranched, hair-
like 'protofeathers' preserved around it, which was
probably present on *Compsognathus* as well. The
protofeathers could well have acted as insulation,
suggesting that compsognathids, and other coelurosaurs
with protofeathers, may have developed 'warm-
bloodedness'.

ID FACT FILE

LENGTH:
2 m (6½ ft)

WEIGHT:
13 kg (30 lb)

TIME:
Late Jurassic

CLASSIFICATION:
Saurischia
Theropoda
Tetanurae
Coelurosauria

DESCRIPTION:
Small lightly built biped. Small head with large teeth and a blunt snout. Neck long. Moderately long arms. Slender hind legs. Three large toes. First toe very small. Long tail with stiff tip.

DIET:
Carnivorous, small mammals, lizards

Ornitholestes
(bird thief)

Ornitholestes was a typical small coelurosaur. Coelurosaurs were a group of tetanuran theropods that underwent a spectacular evolutionary radiation in the Late Jurassic to produce such different groups as tyrannosaurids, therizinosaurids, ornithomimids, oviraptorids, dromaeosaurids and even birds.

Amongst other features in common all these dinosaurs have air-filled cavities invading various bones at the back of the

☐ Triassic
248–206 million yrs.

☐ Jurassic
206–144 million yrs.

☐ Cretaceous
144–65 million yrs.

skull and a broad depression surrounding the hole in the skull, in front of the eye. *Ornitholestes* is close to what palaeontologists think the ancestor of these groups would have looked like. It was small and lightly built with a long neck and long grasping hands with curved claws.

Many recent reconstructions of *Ornithlestes* give it a flattened horn on its nose. Recent cleaning of the specimen has shown that this is in error and that the appearance of the base of a nose horn was caused by damage to the snout.

FAMILY ARCHAEOPTERYGIIDAE (AVES)

Archaeopteryx

(ancient feather)

ID FACT FILE

LENGTH:
45 cm (18 in)

WEIGHT:
300 g (11 oz)

TIME:
Late Jurassic

CLASSIFICATION:
Saurischia
Theropoda
Tetanurae, Aves
Coelurosauria

DESCRIPTION:
Small biped.
Triangular head
with pointed
snout. Very long
arms feathered
to form broad
wings. Three-
clawed fingers;
three large toes.
Short, stiff,
feathered tail.

DIET:
Carnivorous,
small animals.

This is perhaps the most famous vertebrate fossil of all because it provided early evidence of animal intermediate in structure between two classes of animal, supporting Darwin's theory of evolution

The stunningly preserved fossils showed *Archaeopteryx* had a coat of feathers and a 'wishbone' or furcula in its shoulder girdle. Amongst modern animals these features can only be found in birds.

☐ Triassic
248–206 million yrs.

☐ Jurassic
206–144 million yrs.

☐ Cretaceous
144–65 million yrs.

FAMILY ARCHAEOPTERYGIIDAE (AVES)

However, *Archaeopteryx* displayed such reptilian
features as teeth and a long bony tail, which no modern
bird has. It soon became clear that amongst reptiles,
Archaeopteryx most closely resembled theropod
dinosaurs. Indeed it is almost a bone for bone match
with the dromaeosaurids (see pp. 218–225), the
closest relatives of the birds. *Archaeopteryx* lived on
small arid islands in a lagoon where it may have
spent its time clambering about in low shrubs. It had
small conical teeth ideal for capturing insects and
other small prey.

FAMILY HYBODONTIDAE (CHONDRICHTHYES)

ID FACT FILE

LENGTH:
2.5 m (8 ft)

TIME:
Middle Triassic to
Late Cretaceous

CLASSIFICATION:
Vertebrata
Chondrichthyes

DESCRIPTION:
Medium-sized, to
large, shark.
Jaws not set
back from snout
tip. Two dorsal
fins each with a
sharp spine.
A pair of small
hooked spines
behind each eye.

DIET:
Carnivorous,
fish, squid-like
molluscs, small
marine reptiles.

Hybodus
(blunt cone-tooth)

Hybodus was perhaps the most abundant shark during the Mesozoic Era. It differed from modern sharks in having jaws that did not protrude when biting. It also lacked the pointed overhanging snout that is typical of modern sharks. Like all sharks, its skeleton was made of cartilage, which quickly decays after death. As a consequence most *Hybodus* fossils are isolated teeth.

☐ Triassic
248–206 million yrs.

■ Jurassic
206–144 million yrs.

■ Cretaceous
144–65 million yrs.

FAMILY HYBODONTIDAE (CHONDRICHTHYES)

Fortunately the exceptional Early Jurassic locality of
Holzmaden, in Germany, has preserved a number of
complete skeletons. From these we know that it had
two dorsal fins, each with a sharp spine in front of it.
There were also small hook-shaped spines above and
behind each eye.

The tall pointed teeth show that *Hybodus* was adapted
to catching and tearing fast-moving and slippery prey.
In this respect, *Hybodus* differs from its close relatives
which had flat crushing teeth adapted for dealing
with shell-fish.

ID FACT FILE

LENGTH:
2.5 m (8 ft)

TIME:
Early Jurassic

CLASSIFICATION:
Reptilia
Diapsida
Ichthyosauria

DESCRIPTION:
Torpedo-shaped body. Snout long and thin with many pointed teeth. Triangular, paddle-like limbs. Front limbs much larger than hind limbs. Triangular dorsal fin. Crescent-shaped tail fin.

DIET:
Carnivorous, Fish, and squid-like molluscs.

Triassic
248–206 million yrs.

Jurassic
206–144 million yrs.

Cretaceous
144–65 million yrs.

Stenopterygius
(narrow fin)

Stenopterygius was a common member of the most highly adapted group of marine reptiles, the icthyosaurs. Their name means 'fish lizard' and indeed they looked more like fish than reptiles. Nevertheless they lacked gills and had many reptilian skeletal traits. Very fine specimens of *Stenopterygius* from Holzmaden in Germany preserve an outline of the soft tissues and show that they had a shark-like dorsal fin and a crescent shaped tail fin. The spinal column has a distinct bend at the tail base with the

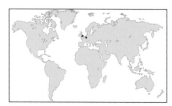

FAMILY STENOPTERYGIIDAE (ICHTHYOSAURIA)

column continuing down into the lower lobe of the
tail. The upper lobe was unsupported by bone.
Other *Stenopterygius* skeletons show numerous
embryonic skeletons inside, some preserved half
way out of their mother's birth canal! This is proof
that ichthyosaurs spent their entire lives at sea and
did not return to land to lay eggs. Its snout formed a
long beak lined with sharp teeth. It was clearly a fast
swimming hunter.

ID FACT FILE

LENGTH:
3.5 m (11½ ft)

TIME:
Late Jurassic

CLASSIFICATION:
Reptilia
Diapsida
Ichthyosauria

DESCRIPTION:
Short, thick-bodied ichthyosaur. Head with long thin snout and enormous eyes. Short broad paddle-like limbs. Narrow tail base with deep crescent-shaped tail fin.

DIET:
Carnivorous, Fish, and squid-like molluscs.

Opthalmosaurus
(eye lizard)

Opthalmosaurus lived after *Stenopterygius* (see pp. 90–91). It differed from that ichthyosaur in having broader paddles, a more compact body and a sharper kink in its tail suggesting that the tail fin was shorter and deeper, like that of a swordfish. All these features indicate that *Opthalmosaurus* was a very fast swimmer indeed.

Another peculiar feature of *Opthalmosaurus* was its enormous eyes. The size of ichthyosaur eye can be

Triassic
248–206 million yrs.

Jurassic
206–144 million yrs.

Cretaceous
144–65 million yrs.

estimated accurately because they were reinforced with large bony plates, which formed a ring around the iris.

An *Opthalmosaurus* eyeball was almost 25 cm (10 in) across, making it one largest of the animal kingdom and certainly the largest relative to body size. This big eye suggests that it could see in low light conditions so perhaps it was diving to great depths. Further evidence for deep diving comes from their bone micro-texture, which shows frequent damage caused by decompression sickness, or the 'bends'.

ID FACT FILE

LENGTH:
3 m (10 ft)

TIME:
Early Jurassic

CLASSIFICATION:
Reptilia, Diapsida
Sauropterygia
Plesiosauria

DESCRIPTION:
Head small and
short with long
pointed teeth.
Neck several times
longer than the
skull. Body short
and wide. Limbs
form elongate
paddles. Tail short.

DIET:
Carnivorous, Fish,
and squid-like
molluscs.

Triassic
248–206 million yrs.

Jurassic
206–144 million yrs.

Cretaceous
144–65 million yrs.

Plesiosaurus
(nearly a lizard)

Plesiosaurians were a successful group of
aquatic reptiles during the Jurassic and
Cretaceous. There were two basic types, the
long necked small-headed plesiosaurs and
the short-necked large headed pliosaurs.

Plesiosaurus was an early
example of the former group.
It had a flexible neck that was
about as long as its body.
Plesiosaurs had long sharp
teeth for catching slippery
prey such as fish or squid-like
animals.

There has been controversy
about how plesiosaurs may
have swum. Underwater

rowing is not feasible without paddles that can be folded up, and underwater flying seems to be ruled out by the structure of the hip and shoulder girdles, which do not allow the paddles to be lifted above horizontal. The best solution seems to be that they swam like modern sea lions, which use a combination of rowing and flying like motions of their paddles to power them through the water.

FAMILY ROMAELOSAURIDAE (PLESIOSAURIA)

ID FACT FILE

LENGTH:
6 m (20 ft)

TIME:
Early Jurassic

CLASSIFICATION:
Reptilia, Diapsida
Sauropterygia
Plesiosauria

DESCRIPTION:
Long, broad head
with large teeth.
Neck slightly
longer than the
skull. Body short
and wide. Limbs
form elongate
paddles. Tail short.

DIET:
Fish, other
marine reptiles.

Rhomaelosaurus

(robust lizard)

Rhomaelosaurus was an early pliosaur, the big-headed plesiosaurians that specialized on larger prey than their long-necked ancestors. It displays some signs of its ancestry as its neck is relatively longer than in later pliosaurs, indeed it is slightly longer than the length of the skull. In all species however the head is broad, flat and relatively larger than in plesiosaurs.

□ Triassic
248–206 million yrs.

■ Jurassic
206–144 million yrs.

■ Cretaceous
144–65 million yrs.

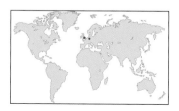

FAMILY ROMAELOSAURIDAE (PLESIOSAURIA)

The ends of the jaws bear a rounded expansion. This expanded tip was armed with a rosette of enlarged, interlocking teeth much like those of modern crocodiles. *Rhomaelosaurus* probably used them in a similar manner, holding tightly onto its prey while the animal rolled in the water, thus tearing off a large chunk of flesh. Its prey would have included large fish and other marine reptiles.

ID FACT FILE

LENGTH:
3 m (10 ft)

TIME:
Middle to
Late Jurassic

CLASSIFICATION:
Reptilia, Diapsida
Archosauria
Crurotarsi
Crocodyliformes

DESCRIPTION:
Long, thin snouted
crocodile. Skin
smooth. Limbs
form small
paddles. Half-moon
shaped tail fin.

DIET:
Carnivorous, fish.

Metriorhynchus

(middle [-sized] beak)

Metriorhynchus was a sea-going relative of the modern crocodiles. It was very well adapted to its marine existence and probably only ventured onto land to lay its eggs. Although found mainly in Europe, relatives of *Metriorhynchus* spread throughout the warm tropical seas of the world.

Its limbs had become modified into paddles, it had lost the bony armour

☐ Triassic
248–206 million yrs.

☐ Jurassic
206–144 million yrs.

☐ Cretaceous
144–65 million yrs.

FAMILY METRIORHYNCHIDAE (CROCODYLIFORMES)

plates that all other crurotarsans have (see *Postosuchus*, pp. 26–27), and it had developed a fish-like tail. We can tell that the tail was modified in this manner because, like ichthyosaurs, the tail contains a strong downward bend.

Its long, narrow snout and sharp conical teeth are typical of fish hunting animals and this is without doubt what it fed upon. The narrow jaws reduced water resistance and allowed them to be closed quickly underwater. The diapsid skull openings had become very large in this animal suggesting that its jaw muscles were very long and consequently that its gape was wide.

ID FACT FILE

LENGTH:
Wingspan 60 cm
(24 in)

TIME:
Late Jurassic

CLASSIFICATION:
Reptilia, Diapsida
Archosauria
Ornithodira
Pterosauria
Rhamphorhynch-
oidea

DESCRIPTION:
Small flying
reptile. Long arms
with three free
fingers, long
fourth finger
supporting wing
membrane;
second membrane
between legs.
Tail long with
thickened tip.

DIET:
Carnivorous,
insects.

Sordes

(devil)

Sordes was a tiny pterosaur (flying reptile)
related to *Rhamphorynchus* (see pp.
102–103). The spectacular preservation
of its remains (which are found in shales
that were laid down in an ancient lake)
has helped clear up many aspects of
pterosaur anatomy.

These fossils show that *Sordes* had a pelt
of hair-like filaments. This would have
insulated the animal, indicating that the
animal was endothermic ('warm-blooded').

Triangle Triassic
248–206 million yrs.

Triangle Jurassic
206–144 million yrs.

Triangle Cretaceous
144–65 million yrs.

Since flying is such an energy demanding activity it is likely that all pterosaurs were hairy and endothermic. The fossils also show that the wing membrane stretched from the tip of the elongated fourth finger to the ankle. A second membrane spanned the space between its hind legs and it was held tight by the spine-like fifth toe of each foot. These membranes were supported by stiff fibres that ran from the arms and legs to the trailing edge of the membranes.

It differed from *Rhamphorhynchus* in having vertically oriented teeth (for catching insect prey) and by lacking an expanded tail-vane.

ID FACT FILE

WINGSPAN:
1.75 m (6 ft)

TIME:
Late Jurassic

CLASSIFICATION:
Reptilia, Diapsida
Archosauria
Ornithodira
Pterosauria
Rhamphorhynch-
oidea

DESCRIPTION:
Small flying
reptile. Like
Sordes but with
sharp, pointed
snout tip and a
diamond-shaped
tail-vane.

DIET:
Carnivorous,
fish.

Rhamphorhynchus
(beaked snout)

Rhamphorhynchus was without doubt a fishing pterosaur. Its jaws bore a pointed beak at their tips and were filled with long, forward pointing, spiky teeth that produced a structure excellent for spearing and holding slippery prey.

The downward bend of its lower jaw suggests that it may have skimmed surface waters while flying, as some seabirds do.

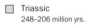
☐ Triassic
248–206 million yrs.

☐ Jurassic
206–144 million yrs.

☐ Cretaceous
144–65 million yrs.

FAMILY RHAMPHORHYNCHIDAE (RHAMPHORHYNCHOIDEA)

Most remains of this pterosaur come from the famous Solnhoffen Limestone, a lagoonal deposit that also preserves *Archaeopteryx* (see pp. 86–87) amongst other well known extinct creatures. The fine preservation of this deposit has produced a number of specimens with impressions of the wing membrane.

These show that the wing was narrow for most of its length and that many rod-like fibres stiffened it. The tail also had a diamond-shaped vane at its tip, which was probably used as a rudder during flight.

ID FACT FILE

WINGSPAN:
50 cm (20 in)

TIME:
Late Jurassic

CLASSIFICATION:
Reptilia, Diapsida
Archosauria
Ornithodira
Pterosauria
Rhamphorhynch-
oidea

DESCRIPTION:
Small flying reptile.
Head short, deep
and broad. Arms
long. Three free
fingers. Fourth
finger very long
supporting wing
membrane.
Second membrane
stretches between
the legs. Four toes
with claws, fifth
toe spine-like. Tail
shorter than body.

DIET:
Carnivorous,
insects.

Anurognathus

(tail-less jaw)

The unusual name of this pterosaur refers
to the resemblance of its jaws to the jaws
of a frog (called anurans by scientists).

Unlike most other pterosaurs *Anurognathus*
had a short broad snout that
would not had been useful for
catching aquatic animals but would
have been good for catching flying
insects.

Thus *Anurognathus* may have
lived further inland than other
pterosaurs. This would explain why
only one skeleton has ever been
found, whereas the lagoonal
deposits in which it was found

☐ Triassic
248–206 million yrs.

☐ Jurassic
206–144 million yrs.

☐ Cretaceous
144–65 million yrs.

have produced dozens of *Pterodactylus* and *Rhamphorhynchus* skeletons. *Anurognathus* had a very short tail like pterodactyloid pterosaurs but also had a long spine-like fifth toe and short neck vertebrae characteristic of rhamphornychoids. For these reasons *Anurognathus* is classified as a ramphorhynchoid that evolved a short tail at the same time as pterodactyloids.

Pterodactlyus

(wing finger)

ID FACT FILE

WINGSPAN:
2.5 m (8 ft)

TIME:
Late Jurassic

CLASSIFICATION:
Reptilia, Diapsida
Archosauria
Ornithodira
Pterosauria
Pterodactyloidea

DESCRIPTION:
Small flying reptile.
Head with long
narrow jaws. Neck
long. Arms long.
Three free fingers.
Fourth finger very
long supporting
wing membrane.
Second membrane
stretches between
the legs. Four
webbed toes. Tail
reduced to stump.

DIET:
Carnivorous, small
invertebrates.

Petrodactylus was an early member of
the pterodactyloid group of pterosaurs
which completely supplanted the
rhamphorhynchoids in the Cretaceous.

Pterodactyloids differ from
rhamphorhynchoids in having a reduced
stump for a tail and in having only four
toes (the spine-like fifth toe is missing).
Pterodactylus had a rather
simple cranial design
without any of the
extravagant crests of
other pterodactyloids.

☐ Triassic
248–206 million yrs.

▨ Jurassic
206–144 million yrs.

■ Cretaceous
144–65 million yrs.

FAMILY PTERODACTYLIDAE (PTERODACTYLOIDEA)

Soft tissue impressions show that it had broad wings that attach to the knee and webbed feet. It had a long neck and a long, narrow snout with small, conical teeth placed at its tip.

The jaws resemble a pair of forceps and it has been suggested that they were used as such to pull worms and other soft bodied invertebrates from the mud of tidal flats. This is certainly plausible, and its webbed hindfeet are also consistent with a shorebird-like lifestyle.

ID FACT FILE

LENGTH:
10 cm (4 in)

TIME:
Early Jurassic

CLASSIFICATION:
Synapsida
Therapsida
Mammaliaformes

DESCRIPTION:
Tiny sprawling
quadruped.
Similar to a
modern shrew.
Probably hairy.
Ears probably
simple holes.
Fingers and Toes
five. Moderately
long thin tail.

DIET:
Carnivorous,
insects and
other small
invertebrates.

Triassic
248–206 million yrs.

Jurassic
206–144 million yrs.

Cretaceous
144–65 million yrs.

Morganucodon
(Morgan's tooth)

Morganucodon is often portrayed as one of
the earliest known mammals, however this
is not strictly true in modern classifications.
It was undoubtedly a close relative of
modern mammals, and would have looked
a lot like a shrew. Nevertheless it retained
accessory lower jaw-bones besides the
main tooth-bearing bone.

In all modern mammals these jaw bones
are transferred to the middle ear. For this
reason *Morganucodon* is

classified as a mammaliaform (the larger group that includes mammals and their close relatives) but not a true mammal.

Given its small size and apparently warm-blooded metabolism, it was almost certainly had a pelt of fur for insulation. It had sharp pointed teeth that were differentiated into incisors, canines and molars for processing its invertebrate prey.

Its remains have been found in the sediment filling ancient cave systems of South-west Britain, much like those of *Thecodontosaurus* (see pp. 12–13).

ID FACT FILE

LENGTH:
2 m (6½ ft)

TIME:
Early Cretaceous

CLASSIFICATION:
Ornithischia
Thyreophora
Ankylosauria

DESCRIPTION:
Small, heavy bodied quadruped. Head short and broad with a deep, narrow snout. Multiple rows of small keeled plates over the back. A pair of large plates on the neck and another over the shoulders. Tear-drop shaped spikes on each side of the hips.

DIET:
Herbivorous.

Minmi

(from Minmi [Crossing])

Minmi was an unusual small ankylosaur from Australia. Ankylosaurs are heavily armoured relatives of the stegosaurs (see pp. 34–41). It does not fit readily into any of the main ankylosaurid families and probably represents a unique Australian group.

The spinal column contained unique bones that lay on both sides of each vertebra. These were originally thought to be bases for muscles that could move

□ Triassic
248–206 million yrs.

■ Jurassic
206–144 million yrs.

■ Cretaceous
144–65 million yrs.

the dorsal armour plates. We now know that the dorsal armour was not especially large or elaborate and these odd bones were more likely to be ossified tendons. The skull of *Minmi* was shaped like a pentagonal box with a very narrow snout projecting from its front. Like polacanthids and ankylosaurids the rear corners of the skull bore little horns.

Gut contents show that *Minmi* was a herbivore that finely chopped its food before swallowing and did not use a gizzard with stomach stones to further process its food.

ID FACT FILE

LENGTH:
5 m (16½ ft)

TIME:
Early Cretaceous

CLASSIFICATION:
Ornithischia
Thyreophora
Ankylosauria

DESCRIPTION:
Medium-sized,
heavy bodied
quadruped. Body
low and broad. A
row of flat spikes
on each side.
Numerous
keeled plates on
the back and tail.

DIET:
Herbivorous

Hylaeosaurus
(woodland lizard)

Hylaeosaurus was one of the original trio of extinct animals that Richard Owen proposed to call the Dinosauria in 1842. The other two were *Megalosaurus* and *Iguanodon*. Unfortunately no new remains of *Hylaeosaurus* have come to light since its original discovery so it has remained a poorly-known beast.

What is known is that it was an ankylosaur, one of the heavily armoured four-legged ornithischians.

Triassic
248–206 million yrs.

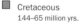
Jurassic
206–144 million yrs.

Cretaceous
144–65 million yrs.

Its armour is not completely known but we do know that the tail was studded with peaked, oval-shaped horny plates or scutes, and that large, flat, triangular spikes protected its flanks. Such lateral spikes are characteristic of both polocanthid and nodosaurid ankylosaurs. No trace of the large shield that occurs over the pelvic region of polacanthids has ever been found, so it is likely that *Hylaeosaurus* did not have one.

Hylaeosaurus is thought to be a primitive nodosaurid. Nodosaurids had narrow beaks and rounded skulls without any horns. They also lacked the tail club of ankylosaurids.

ID FACT FILE

LENGTH:
5 m (16½ ft)

WEIGHT:
900 kg (2,000 lb)

TIME:
Early Cretaceous

CLASSIFICATION:
Ornithischia
Thyreophora
Ankylosauria

DESCRIPTION:
Low, broad body
armoured with
plates: neck and
shoulders with a
series of large
lateral spikes;
smaller studs
surrounding back
and tail. Tail long
and flexible.

DIET:
Herbivorous

Sauropelta
(lizard skin)

Sauropelta was a typical nodosaurid ankylosaur. Their skulls were more elongate than other ankylosaurs and had narrower beaks. The downward posture of the skull indicates that *Sauropelta* fed close to ground level, and the narrow beaks suggest that they were more selective browsers than the broad-mouthed grazing ankylosaurids (eg. *Euoplocephalus*, see pp. 120–121).

As in all ankylosaurians the teeth were minute and only useful for the coarsest

☐ Triassic
248–206 million yrs.

■ Jurassic
206–144 million yrs.

■ Cretaceous
144–65 million yrs.

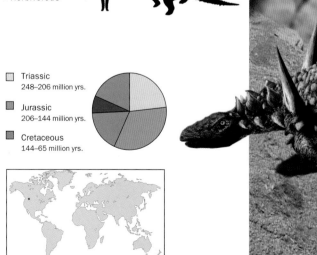

shredding of their food. Much of the food processing would have taken place in the large guts housed in their barrel-shaped bellies. With their large guts, and stout limbs these would not have been speedy animals and would have relied heavily on their armour for protection.

The neck and shoulders of *Sauropelta*, were armed with very large conical spikes that would have made it very difficult for a predator to attack from the front. The rest of the back, hips and tail were covered with a mosaic of keeled plates surrounded by smaller studs. Unlike *Gastonia* (see pp. 118–119) the studs over the hips were not fused into a shield).

ID FACT FILE

LENGTH:
7 m (23 ft)

WEIGHT:
3.5 tons

TIME:
Late Cretaceous

CLASSIFICATION:
Ornithischia
Thyreophora
Ankylosauria

DESCRIPTION:
Large, armoured
quadruped. Front
part of the body
armed with large,
forward-pointing,
lateral spikes,
rectangular plates
and smaller studs
around back and
tail.

DIET:
Herbivorous

Edmontonia
(from Edmonton)

Edmontonia was an advanced nodosaurid.
Unlike the earlier *Sauropelta* (see pp.
114–115), it had a complete bony palate
separating the mouth cavity from the
nasal passages. This would have allowed
it to breathe whilst it was eating. This
would have helped it feed continuously,
which it may needed to do, if
it had a warm blooded
metabolism. Alternatively it
could have lengthened the
nasal chambers to improve its
sense of smell or to make
room for water reclaiming
structures.

☐ Triassic
248–206 million yrs.

☐ Jurassic
206–144 million yrs.

☐ Cretaceous
144–65 million yrs.

FAMILY NODOSAURIDAE (ANKYLOSAURIA)

An interesting feature of the armour of *Edmontonia* is that it is concentrated at the font end of its body. This implies that the animal could not have remained passive in the face of an attack. Instead it would have had to keep moving so that its front end faced the would-be predator. Indeed the shoulder spines are particularly massive and point forwards suggesting that *Edmontonia* may have lunged forwards at its attackers.

Gastonia
(named after Robert Gaston)

This is the best known member of a newly-recognized family of ankylosaurians called polacanthids. Previously polacanthids had been classified with the nodosaurids because they lacked the tail club of ankylosaurids and had large nodosaurid-like lateral spikes.

The discovery of *Gastonia* showed that they had a number of ankylosaurid features such as a skull that is highest in front of the eyes, four triangular horns projecting from its rear corners of the skull, and fused half rings of armour protecting

☐ Triassic
248–206 million yrs.

▨ Jurassic
206–144 million yrs.

▧ Cretaceous
144–65 million yrs.

FAMILY POLACANTHIDAE (ANKYLOSAURIA)

the neck. So they are in someway intermediates between the two well known ankylosaurian families. They also had some peculiar features of their own such as a solidly fused shield of armour covering the hips. *Gastonia* had an additional row of dorsal spikes, each side of the midline, that curved up and out. With so many spikes *Gastonia* would have been a very difficult animal to approach.

ID FACT FILE

LENGTH:
6 m (20 ft)

WEIGHT:
3 tons

TIME:
Late Cretaceous

CLASSIFICATION:
Ornithischia
Thyreophora
Ankylosauria

DESCRIPTION:
Large, squat, wide-bodied quadruped. Head short and broad with a short horn on each rear corner. Neck protected by fused half-rings of bone. Body covered by bands of bony plates and conical studs. Large pair of studs above shoulders and on tail.

DIET:
Herbivorous

◻ Triassic
248–206 million yrs.

◼ Jurassic
206–144 million yrs.

◼ Cretaceous
144–65 million yrs.

Euoplocephalus
(truly armoured head)

Euoplocephalus had one of the most bizarre body-shapes of any dinosaur. It had enormous guts held in a very wide abdominal cavity. Add to this a back that was almost as flat as a table, together with short, stumpy legs and you have an animal that would have looked ludicrous in front view.

FAMILY ANKYLOSAURIDAE (ANKYLOSAURIA)

It was heavily armoured with bands of small studs
set between larger keeled plates and stout spikes.
The front half of the tail was similarly armoured but the
last half was bare, except for a large rounded bony club
at its tip. There were no large lateral spikes that are
present in nodosaurids and polacanthids but it did share
fused half-rings of neck armour with polacanthids. It
even had bony eyelids that, when closed, would shield
its eyes. This obviously slow animal would have had
to rely on its armour to protect it from predators,
while using its tail club as a bone-crushing weapon.

ID FACT FILE

LENGTH:
11 m (36 ft)

WEIGHT:
4 tons

TIME:
Late Cretaceous

CLASSIFICATION:
Ornithischia
Thyreophora
Ankylosauria

DESCRIPTION:
Like
Euoplocephalus
but without large
conical studs
over shoulders,
larger horns on
the head and
side-facing
nostrils.

DIET:
Herbivorous

Ankylosaurus

(stiffened lizard)

Like many other dinosaurs (eg. *Anatotitan*, *Tyrannosaurus* and *Triceratops*), from the very end of the age of Dinosaurs, *Ankylosaurus* was among the largest of its group. It was very similar in overall appearance to *Euoplocephalus* (see pp. 120–121), the main difference being that its nostrils were small and placed on the sides of the snout,

☐ Triassic
248–206 million yrs.

☐ Jurassic
206–144 million yrs.

☐ Cretaceous
144–65 million yrs.

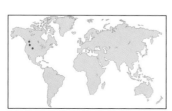

FAMILY ANKYLOSAURIDAE (ANKYLOSAURIA)

rather than being large and forward facing. In both genera the internal nasal passages were particularly convoluted and were separated from the mouth cavity by a secondary palate. A secondary palate allowed the animal to continue breathing while food was processed in the mouth, perhaps because it had an elevated metabolism.

Like *Euoplocephalus* the vertebrae from the last half of the tail interlocked to form a stiff immobile rod, the end of which, bore a large bony club. In contrast the tail base was quite flexible so that it could wield the end of its tail like a mace.

ID FACT FILE

LENGTH:
3 m (10 ft)

WEIGHT:
75 kg (165 lb)

TIME:
Late Cretaceous

CLASSIFICATION:
Ornithischia,
Neornithischia
Marginocephalia
Pachycephalo-
sauria

DESCRIPTION:
Small biped with a
large head and
short neck. Skull
roof thick, pitted
and ornamented.
Back of head with a
rim of bony knobs.
Arms short and
slender. Hands
unknown. Body,
hips and base of
tail very broad.
Long stiff tail.
Feet with four toes

DIET:
Herbivorous

☐ Triassic
248–206 million yrs.

◼ Jurassic
206–144 million yrs.

◼ Cretaceous
144–65 million yrs.

Homalocephale
(same [-thickness] head)

This dinosaur is a primitive member of
the Pachycephalosauria a group closely
related to the Ceratopsia. Like them these
animals have a bony lump on each cheek
and shelf overhanging the back of the head.
This shelf was decorated with a row of
small knobs.

All pachycephalosaurians, including
Homalocephale, have thickened skull
roofs. However in *Homalocephale* the
skull roof remained flat, rather than
bulging into a central dome as it did in

the Pachycephalosauridae. *Homalocephale* is one of the few Pachycephalosaurians for which a relatively complete skeleton is known. Its forelimbs were short and the animal was committed to bipedal locomotion. The ribcage was extremely wide, making room for very enlarged guts and giving the animal an obese appearance. These well-developed guts made up for its small weak teeth, which could do little more than pluck and coarsely shred its leafy food.

FAMILY PACHYCEPHALOSAURIDAE (PACHYCEPHALOSAURIA)

ID FACT FILE

LENGTH:
2 m (6½ ft)

WEIGHT:
30 kg (66 lb)

TIME:
Late Cretaceous

CLASSIFICATION:
Ornithischia
Neornithischia
Marginocephalia
Pachycephalo-
sauria

DESCRIPTION:
Small wide-
bodied biped.
Head large
bearing a
rounded dome
on top a shelf
with small knobs
at the rear.

DIET:
Herbivorous

Stegoceras
(roof horn)

This is one of the more common pachycephalosaurians and yet most of the fossils are just the thick skull roofs. Very few complete skulls are known and only bits and pieces from the rest of the skeleton have been found. The skull roof bulged upwards into a dome of solid bone.

However, unlike more advanced pachy-cephalosaurids, such as *Pachycephalo-saurus* (see pp. 128–129), the dome did

☐ Triassic
248–206 million yrs.

☐ Jurassic
206–144 million yrs.

☐ Cretaceous
144–65 million yrs.

not cover the entire roof of the skull and the overhanging shelf at the back of the skull remained present.

It also maintained the original upper skull holes of diapsid reptiles although there were very reduced in size. *Stegoceras* domes come in two distinct types, one quite low and flat, the other quite tall and rounded. These types may correspond to females and males and suggest that some kind of display or combat rituals occurred between *Stegoceras* males.

ID FACT FILE

LENGTH:
Approx. 8 m (26 ft)

TIME:
Late Cretaceous

CLASSIFICATION:
Ornithischia
Neornithischia
Marginocephalia
Pachycephalo-
sauria

DESCRIPTION:
Probably a wide-
bodied biped.
Skull roof
enormously
thickened into a
dome. Dome
extends to the
posterior rim of
the skull. Roof of
snout with a
cluster of conical
knobs, back of
skull with clusters
of rounded knobs.

DIET:
Herbivorous

Pachycephalosaurus
(thick-headed lizard)

Pachycephalosaurus was among the last
and largest of the dome-headed dinosaur
group. Its large dome fully encompassed
the bones of the skull roof and obliterated
the holes that are usually present at the
back of the skull in diapsid reptiles.

The skull was decorated with more knobs,
and stout spikes than other pachycephalosaurs. These formed clusters around the
back of the skull and over the top of the
snout.

☐ Triassic
  248–206 million yrs.

☐ Jurassic
  206–144 million yrs.

■ Cretaceous
  144–65 million yrs.

The microtexture of the bone that forms the dome seems well adapted for coping with large, front-on impact forces.

This supports the hypothesis that the heads were used as battering rams. The animals may have butted heads with each other like modern bighorn sheep do. However, their rounded domes were likely to produce glancing blows. It is more likely that they butted each other on the flanks in territorial battles or butted threatening predators in defence.

ID FACT FILE

LENGTH:
1.5 m (5 ft)

WEIGHT:
15 kg (33 ft)

TIME:
Early Cretaceous

CLASSIFICATION:
Ornithischia
Neornithischia
Marginocephalia
Ceratopsia

DESCRIPTION:
Small, stout biped.
Large, short,
deep head with
parrot-like beak.
Sharp cheek
projections. Four
fingers and toes
all with blunt
claws.

DIET:
Herbivorous

Psittacosaurus

(parrot lizard)

Psittacosaurus was a small, bipedal ornithischian that, from the neck back, looked like a fat version of *Hypsilophodon* (see pp. 148–149). However its head betrays its relationship to the giant horned ceratopsians of the Late Cretaceous.

Like all ceratopsians it had a deep, narrow beak (shaped rather like a parrot's beak) with a unique bone, the rostral bone, at

Triassic
248–206 million yrs.

Jurassic
206–144 million yrs.

Cretaceous
144–65 million yrs.

its tip. The rostral bone is not found in anywhere else in the animal kingdom.

It also had a very short shelf-like projection from the back of the head that overhung the articulation between the skull and the neck. In later ceratopsians this shelf would become a large frill.

Several *Psittacosaurus* specimens have been found with clusters of little pebbles preserved in the ribcage. In life these would have been held in a gizzard and would have helped breakdown its food. It is the only ornithischian that is known to have had a gizzard.

LENGTH:
2.5 m (8 ft)

TIME:
Late Cretaceous

CLASSIFICATION:
Ornithischia
Neornithischia
Marginocephalia
Ceratopsia

DESCRIPTION:
Small stout
quadruped. Head
large and deep.
Beak parrot-like.
Wide shelf
projecting back
from rear margin
of skull. Tail short
and deep. Five
toes on all feet.

DIET:
Herbivorous

Leptoceratops
(slender-horned face)

This was a very primitive ceratopsian, or horned dinosaur. It had no trace of any facial horns (despite its name) and the shelf at the back of the head (that was to become the frill of later ceratopsians) was only just a little larger than that of *Psittacosaurus* (see pp. 130–131).

Although it had long hindlegs and short, slender forelimbs it was a quadruped. Its large head and a short tail would have made it too unstable for bipedal locomotion.

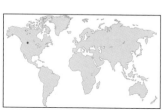

□ Triassic
248–206 million yrs.

■ Jurassic
206–144 million yrs.

■ Cretaceous
144–65 million yrs.

FAMILY PROTOCERATOPSIDAE (CERATOPSIA)

Despite its archaic appearance it lived right at the end of the age of dinosaurs, alongside such advanced ceratopsians as *Triceratops* (see pp. 146–147). A few features such as a big gap between the beak and the cheek teeth, and fusion between the vertebrae of the neck (to help support the massive head) show that *Leptoceratops* was more closely related to advanced ceratopsians than to the similar-looking *Psittacosaurus*.

Like *Protoceratops* (see pp. 134–135) the vertebral spines of the middle of the tail were extra long and may have supported a low hump.

FAMILY PROTOCERATOPSIDAE (CERATOPSIA)

Protoceratops
(before the horned face)

ID FACT FILE

LENGTH:
3 m (10 ft)

WEIGHT:
55 kg (121 lb)

TIME:
Late Cretaceous

CLASSIFICATION:
Ornithischia
Neornithischia
Marginocephalia
Ceratopsia

DESCRIPTION:
Small stout
quadruped. Head
large with deep
parrot-like beak.
Rear margin of
skull with a short
frill. Five toes on
all feet. Short,
leaf-shaped tail

DIET:
Herbivorous

When this dinosaur was first described it
was immediately obvious that it was a link
between the large horned ceratopsids
and more primitive ornithischians.

Like ceratopsids it was a large-headed
four-legged animal. The most obvious
specialization it shared with the ceratopsids
was the extension of the rear margin of
the skull into a frill that covered the neck.
However it lacked the impressive facial
horns of true ceratopsids, although large

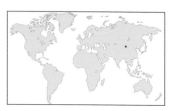

☐ Triassic
248–206 million yrs.

☐ Jurassic
206–144 million yrs.

☐ Cretaceous
144–65 million yrs.

FAMILY PROTOCERATOPSIDAE (CERATOPSIA)

individuals (presumably males) did grow a sharp, pointed bump over their noses. Another primitive feature was the group of teeth in the front of the upper jaw.

Protoceratops lived in desert-like conditions, and its remains are frequently found buried in wind-blown, sand-dune deposits. The spines of the tail vertebrae are extra tall and may have supported a camel-like water, or food, storing hump. The eggs of *Oviraptor* (see pp. 212–213) were, for many years, mistakenly thought to belong to *Protoceratops*.

FAMILY CERATOPSIDAE (CERATOPSIA)

ID FACT FILE

LENGTH:
5.5 m (18 ft)

TIME:
Late Cretaceous

CLASSIFICATION:
Ornithischia
Neornithischia
Marginocephalia
Ceratopsia

DESCRIPTION:
Large heavy bodied quadruped. Head narrow and deep. Deep parrot-like beak. Long horn over the nose and smaller horns over the eyes. Short frill with three six large horns and two smaller horns on its margin. Short sprawled forelegs. All feet with five short toes, blunt claw-like hoofs. Tail short.

DIET:
Herbivorous

☐ Triassic
  248–206 million yrs.

☐ Jurassic
  206–144 million yrs.

☐ Cretaceous
  144–65 million yrs.

Styracosaurus
(spiked lizard)

The latest Cretaceous of North America saw the flowering of the most advanced family of Ceratopsians, the ceratopsids themselves.

Unlike earlier ceratopsians these animals grew impressive horns on their faces and kept a battery of continually growing teeth in their jaws. In this respect their teeth converged upon those of the hadrosaurids but unlike these dinosaurs, ceratopsids'

FAMILY CERATOPSIDAE (CERATOPSIA)

dental batteries formed a set of shearing blades for slicing up food rather than grinding it.

Nevertheless it is clear that they were vegetarians. There are two main groups of ceratopsids, the long-frilled group and the short frilled group. *Styracosaurus* was a member of the short frilled group, which (apart from frill size) were characterized by a long nasal horn and short brow horns.

Styracosaurus was distinctive in that a group of six long horns grew back from the rear margin of its frill, giving it a very spiky appearance indeed!

ID FACT FILE

LENGTH:
6 m (20 ft)

WEIGHT:
2 tons

TIME:
Late Cretaceous

CLASSIFICATION:
Ornithischia
Neornithischia
Marginocephalia
Ceratopsia

DESCRIPTION:
Head narrow and
deep. Deep
parrot-like beak.
Broad nasal horn
that is strongly
bent forward.
Small, irregular
horns over the
eyes. Short frill
with two large
horns on its rear
margin. Body as
in *Styracosaurus*.

DIET:
Herbivorous

☐ Triassic
248–206 million yrs.

■ Jurassic
206–144 million yrs.

■ Cretaceous
144–65 million yrs.

Einiosaurus
(bison lizard)

Einiosaurus was a fairly typical short-
frilled ceratopsid. It was distinctive in
having a wide but flat nasal horn that
curved forward over the tip of the snout.

Growth series show that this unusual
shape grew as the animal got older.
The nasal horn of a juvenile resembled
an adult's in being wide and flat but it
was also erect and did not curve forward.
Adult *Einiosaurus* also had a single pair
of long horns projecting back from the

posterior rim of its frill, a feature shared with
Pachyrhinosaurus (see pp. 140–141).

Like many ceratopsids, *Einiosaurus* also had horns
over each eye but these were low and irregular in
shape. The remains of many individuals have been
found together in a bonebed suggesting that a herd
of *Einiosaurus* had been killed. The distinctive
patterns of horns, that each type of ceratopsid
displays, were probably used as species recognition
structures, much like the crests of hadrosaurids, and
would be useful for
herd formation.

ID FACT FILE

LENGTH:
7 m (23 ft)

TIME:
Late Cretaceous

CLASSIFICATION:
Ornithischia
Neornithischia
Marginocephalia
Ceratopsia

DESCRIPTION:
Head large. Deep
parrot-like beak.
Broad flat pad on
snout. Smaller
pads over eyes.
Short frill. Two
sideways pointing
horns on frill
margin. Three
short horns in
centre of frill.
Body as in
Stryracosaurus.

DIET:
Herbivorous

Pachyrhinosaurus
(thick-nosed lizard)

This was the largest short-frilled ceratopsid.
It had replaced its facial horns with large
bony bosses that were probably covered
by horny pads in life. The nasal boss was
particularly large a formed a large, flat,
pad that dominated the face.

Like the dome of pachycephalosaurs,
the nasal pad could have been used in
butting contests. However the

☐ Triassic
248–206 million yrs.

■ Jurassic
206–144 million yrs.

■ Cretaceous
144–65 million yrs.

FAMILY CERATOPSIDAE (CERATOPSIA)

frill remained spiky with a large horn jutting out on each side and a cluster of three small horns placed in the centre of the frill.

Its remains have been found in far northern North America. Indeed these northerly sites would have been well within the Cretaceous Arctic Circle. This has led to suggestions that herds of *Pachyrhinosaurus* migrated in and out of the Arctic each year. However there is no evidence for such a migration and it is possible that they simply stayed and withstood the Arctic winter.

ID FACT FILE

LENGTH:
5 m (16½ ft)

WEIGHT:
1.7 tons

TIME:
Late Cretaceous

CLASSIFICATION:
Ornithischia
Neornithischia
Marginocephalia
Ceratopsia

DESCRIPTION:
Head narrow and deep. Deep parrot-like beak. Moderately large, erect, nasal horn. Backward-curved horn of variable size over each eye. Long rectangular frill. Frill margin with triangular studs. Extra large studs on the rear corners of the frill. Body as in *Styracosaurus*.

DIET:
Herbivorous

☐ Triassic
248–206 million yrs.

☐ Jurassic
206–144 million yrs.

☐ Cretaceous
144–65 million yrs.

Chasmosaurus
(chasm lizard)

This was a typical long frilled ceratopsid. It face was armoured with a short nose horn and two backward-curving brow horns. The size of the brow horns was variable. In some they were much longer than the nose horn (like *Triceratops*, see pp. 146–147) while in others they were no bigger than the nose horn.

This may represent a sexual difference. The frill of *Chasmosaurus* was quite tall and erect and was long enough to cover the shoulders when the head was lifted.

The frill was pierced by windows that were so big that they reduced the bony part of the frill into a light series of connected struts. The margins of the frill were decorated with pointed triangular bones with particularly large ones at the rear corners of the frill.

Like many dinosaurs the nasal chambers of ceratopsids, including *Chasmosaurus*, were greatly enlarged.

ID FACT FILE

LENGTH:
8 m (26 ft)

WEIGHT:
5 tons

TIME:
Late Cretaceous

CLASSIFICATION:
Ornithischia
Neornithischia
Marginocephalia
Ceratopsia

DESCRIPTION:
Head narrow and
deep. Deep parrot-
like beak. Small
nasal horn. Very
large forward
pointing horns
over each eye. Frill
very long with
smooth margins.
Body as in
Styracosaurus.

DIET:
Herbivorous

Torosaurus
(perforated lizard)

Torosaurus has the distinction of having
the largest skull of any known terrestrial
animal. One skull measures 2.3 m (7½ ft)
in length. Much of this length is taken up
by a very long frill, which unlike other
ceratopsids had smooth margins.

As with other ceratopsids, it was probably
sexually dimorphic. There exist two types
of skull: a large one with erect brow horns,
and a smaller variety with forward pointing
brow horns.

Torosaurus also had a short, conical nasal
horn. It was a contemporary of
Triceratops (see pp. 146–147) but its

- Triassic
  248–206 million yrs.
- Jurassic
  206–144 million yrs.
- Cretaceous
  144–65 million yrs.

fossils are much less common. A recently-discovered forelimb of *Torosaurus* has helped resolve the debate over the posture of the forelimbs of ceratopsids.

It has shown that, unlike the erect hindlimbs, the forelimbs were held in a semi-sprawled position with the elbows bowed outwards and that the forefeet were planted further from the midline than the hindfeet. The significance of this unusual posture is not understood at present.

ID FACT FILE

LENGTH:
9 m (30 ft)

WEIGHT:
6 tons

TIME:
Late Cretaceous

CLASSIFICATION:
Ornithischia
Neornithischia
Marginocephalia
Ceratopsia

DESCRIPTION:
Same as
Torosaurus but
with a short
rounded frill
bordered with
triangular studs.

DIET:
Herbivorous

Triceratops

(three-horned face)

A classic and much loved dinosaur, *Triceratops* is often used as the typical example of a ceratopsian dinosaur. Nevertheless it was quite unusual for the group. It had the typical long brow horns and short nasal horn of a long frilled ceratopsid but its frill was short.

Its frill was also unlike both long and short frilled ceratopsids in being solid and lacking large holes to reduce its weight. Enough similarities with between *Triceratops* and long frilled ceratopsids exist to demonstrate that

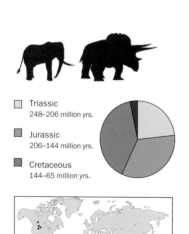

☐ Triassic
248–206 million yrs.

☐ Jurassic
206–144 million yrs.

☐ Cretaceous
144–65 million yrs.

it is a member of the long frilled group that had
evolved an unusual frill. Like most ceratopsids the
margins of the frill were decorated with little
pointed studs. Its large horns were clearly dangerous
weapons that would have helped protect it against
predators. They could have also been used in battles
with other *Triceratops* over territories or mates,
much as modern horned mammals do.

Hypsilophodon
(high-ridge tooth)

ID FACT FILE

LENGTH:
1.4 m (4 ft)

WEIGHT:
10 kg (22 lb)

TIME:
Early Cretaceous

CLASSIFICATION:
Ornithischia
Neornithischia
Ornithopoda

DESCRIPTION:
Medium sized,
lightly-built, biped
with a small
short skull. Arms
short with four
blunt-clawed
fingers and feet
with four toes.

DIET:
Herbivorous

Despite living in the last period of the
Mesozoic Era, *Hypsilophodon* was a
primitive ornithischian that would have
resembled the common ancestor of the
whole group.

Like the ancestral ornithischians, it was a
small, light-weight biped. Its head was
short with a pointed beak,
which retained a row
of teeth in the upper
part. It also had four
digits on both hands
and feet.

☐ Triassic
248–206 million yrs.

☐ Jurassic
206–144 million yrs.

☐ Cretaceous
144–65 million yrs.

Nevertheless some more subtle aspects of its anatomy showed that it was had changed somewhat from the ancestral condition. Its teeth were inset well away from the edge of the jaws creating a space that probably formed cheek pouches in life. The enamel of its teeth was also thicker on one side so that when they were worn down it formed a cutting edge.

These are herbivorous specializations that are present in the earliest ornithischians. It was a small and fleet-footed animal, rather like the gazelle of its day.

Leaellynasaura

(Leaellyn's lizard)

Leaellynasaura was very similar to
Hypsilophodon, differing only in having
ridges on both sides of the teeth (as
opposed solely on the outside) and in
having a flatter lower end of the thigh
bone (femur). *Laellynasaura* is that it
lived in Southern Australia during the
Early Cretaceous when it was well with
in the Antarctic Circle.

Although the Earth's climate was
a lot milder then there is still
evidence that temperatures
dropped below freezing during

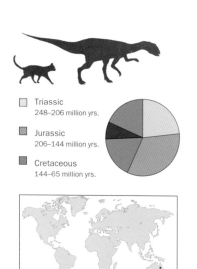

☐ **Triassic**
248–206 million yrs.

▨ **Jurassic**
206–144 million yrs.

■ **Cretaceous**
144–65 million yrs.

the long, dark winters. Even more surprising is that the microtexture of their bones indicate that they grew quickly and continuously to adult size. In a harsh climate this could only be achieved through a 'warm-blooded' metabolism.

The only known skull is a juvenile, it has large eyes and well developed optic lobes in its brain cavity. Some have suggested that the large eyes helped it to see during the dark polar winter but they are typical features of a juvenile animal.

Tenontosaurus

(tendon lizard)

ID FACT FILE

LENGTH:
5 m (16½ ft)

WEIGHT:
300 kg (660 lb)

TIME:
Early Cretaceous

CLASSIFICATION:
Ornithischia
Neornithischia
Ornithopoda
Iguanodontia

DESCRIPTION:
Medium sized,
heavily built biped
or quadruped with
a moderately
large, deep skull.
Hands with three
clawed fingers,
fourth and fifth
finger clawless
stumps. Feet with
four toes. Tail
very long.

DIET:
Herbivorous

The long tail of this dinosaur took up much of its length. Although moderately large, and possibly four-legged, this animal shares many similarities with the small, bipedal *Hypsilophodon*. Indeed some palaeontologists believe that it was a giant hypsilophodontid and should not be classified in the Iguanodontia.

Nevertheless, like *Dryosaurus* (see pp. 44–45), it had no teeth at the front of its jaws and had a deep groove in its thigh

☐ Triassic
248–206 million yrs.

▨ Jurassic
206–144 million yrs.

■ Cretaceous
144–65 million yrs.

bone for strong leg muscles and so is probably a
primitive iguanodontian.

Tenontosaurus was a common herbivore in its time
and place and appears to have been a favourite prey
animal of *Deinonychus* (see pp. 222–223). One
skeleton was found together with a number of
Deinonychus skeletons. Perhaps these were unlucky
members of a pack that were killed by the struggling
Tenontosaurus before it was finally brought down.

FAMILY UNNAMED (IGUANODONTIA)

Muttaburrasaurus
(lizard from Muttaburra)

ID FACT FILE

LENGTH:
9 m (30 ft)

WEIGHT:
4 tons

TIME:
Early Cretaceous

CLASSIFICATION:
Ornithischia
Neornithischia
Ornithopoda
Iguanodontia

DESCRIPTION:
Large, heavy-bodied
biped. Large head
with toothless
beak at front and
inflated nasal
chamber on snout.
Neck moderately
long. Arms long.
Probably five
fingers. Three
short toes

DIET:
Herbivorous

Muttaburrasaurus is one of the few
Australian dinosaurs known from a
largely complete skeleton. It was a large,
heavy-bodied plant eater that superficially
resembled *Iguanodon* (see pp. 156–157).

Nevertheless many aspects of its anatomy
show that, amongst the iguanodontians, it
was not a particularly close relative of
Iguanodon. Instead *Muttaburrasaurus*
may be a member of an endemic Australian
family that we know little about.

☐ Triassic
248–206 million yrs.

☐ Jurassic
206–144 million yrs.

☐ Cretaceous
144–65 million yrs.

FAMILY UNNAMED (IGUANODONTIA)

Muttaburrasaurus certainly has a number of features that make it quite distinct amongst iguanodontians. Most striking were the inflated nasal chambers that produced a dorsal bulge along the profile of the snout. These may have functioned as resonating chambers to produce a loud call or they may have warmed up inspired air.

Another intriguing aspect was its enlarged jaw closing muscles and its teeth, which formed scissor-like shearing blades. So, like a ceratopsian dinosaur, it may have chopped its food up rather than grinding it as did other iguanodontians.

ID FACT FILE

LENGTH:
11 m (36 ft)

WEIGHT:
5.5 tons

TIME:
Early Cretaceous

CLASSIFICATION:
Ornithischia
Neornithischia
Ornithopoda
Iguanodontia

DESCRIPTION:
Large, heavy-bodied. Long head with toothless beak. Forelegs smaller than hindlegs. Forefeet with large spike, central digits in a single unit, small grasping inner digit.

DIET:
Herbivorous

Iguanodon

(iguana tooth)

This was a common and widespread herbivore in the Early Cretaceous.
It has been found in North America and Asia but it is in Europe where it becomes very common, making up most of the Early Cretaceous dinosaur finds of that continent. It is not surprising then that some of the earliest dinosaur finds belonged to this dinosaur.

It was a large iguanodontian that had developed long strong forelimbs. In all

Triassic
248–206 million yrs.

Jurassic
206–144 million yrs.

Cretaceous
144–65 million yrs.

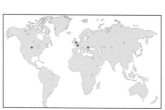

probability the animal had become a quadruped but it would have been capable of some bipedal locomotion.

The thumb had been transformed into a large conical spike that would have made a dangerous offensive weapon. The middle digits of the hand supported the weight of the animal, while the fifth digit formed a slender and flexible finger that could grasp vegetation and bring to the mouth. Only three toes with blunt claws remained on the stocky hindleg.

ID FACT FILE

LENGTH:
6 m (20 ft)

WEIGHT:
1 ton

TIME:
Early Cretaceous

CLASSIFICATION:
Ornithischia
Neornithischia
Ornithopoda
Iguanodontia

DESCRIPTION:
Large, heavy-
bodied. Tall sail
or narrow hump
over body, hips
and tail. Forelegs
smaller than
hindlegs. Forefeet
with small spike
and grasping
inner digit.

DIET:
Herbivorous

Ouranosaurus

(brave lizard)

This dinosaur was found in the sands of
the Sahara desert. Of course at the time
of burial the desert did not exist and there
was plenty of vegetation and fresh water.

Nevertheless it was a tropical place and
during the Cretaceous the days could have
got very hot. This may give some clue to the
function of the most distinctive feature of
Ouranosaurus, the tall crest running
along its back.

☐ Triassic
  248–206 million yrs.

■ Jurassic
  206–144 million yrs.

■ Cretaceous
  144–65 million yrs.

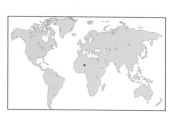

FAMILY IGUANODONTIDAE (IGUANODONTIA)

This crest was formed from enormously elongated spines growing out of the top of each of its trunk vertebrae. Usually these are reconstructed as supporting a skin-covered sail but a large fatty hump is equally plausible. A sail could act as a radiator to help cool the animal, whereas a hump could insulate the torso from the overhead sun, as well as store fat reserves.

Like the hadrosaurids, *Ouranosaurus* had a broad duck-like beak for cropping plants.

FAMILY HADROSAURIDAE (IGUANODONTIA)

ID FACT FILE

LENGTH:
9 m (30 ft)

TIME:
Late Cretaceous

CLASSIFICATION:
Ornithischia
Neornithischia
Ornithopoda
Iguanodontia

DESCRIPTION:
Large, heavy
quadruped. Large
hump on snout
above nose.
Forelimbs shorter
and slimmer than
hindlimbs.
Serrated frill of
skin on back.
Moderately short,
straight, deep tail.

DIET:
Herbivorous

Gryposaurus
(hook [-nosed] lizard)

The Hadrosauridae was the dominant
family of plant eaters in the Northern
Hemisphere of the Late Cretaceous.
They differ from other iguanodontians in
lacking a thumb, or thumbspike, and in
having batteries of small teeth, all tightly
packed together, with old worn teeth
being continually replaced by new teeth
growing from underneath. In this way the
teeth formed a single, large, grinding
surface in each jaw, that was maintained
at all times.

■ Triassic
248–206 million yrs.

■ Jurassic
206–144 million yrs.

■ Cretaceous
144–65 million yrs.

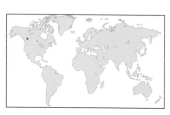

FAMILY HADROSAURIDAE (IGUANODONTIA)

Hadrosaurids also had broad and toothless beaks in front of their dental batteries, which has given them their nickname: duckbilled dinosaurs.

Many hadrosaurids had crests adorning their heads, although *Gryposaurus* did not. It did have a swollen bump over the top of its large nostrils. An even larger depression encircling the nostrils suggests that in life there was a very large outer nasal chamber that was covered by soft tissues. Quite why this is so is not known for sure, although it may have formed a resonating chamber that gave it a loud and distinctive voice when calling to other *Gryposaurus*.

ID FACT FILE

LENGTH:
13 m (10 ft)

WEIGHT:
7.5 tons

TIME:
Late Cretaceous

CLASSIFICATION:
Ornithischia
Neornithischia
Ornithopoda
Iguanodontia

DESCRIPTION:
Like *Gryposaurus*
but with a longer
lower head. No
nasal hump and
a wider beak.

DIET:
Herbivorous

Anatotitan
(duck giant)

Anatotitan was one a very large
hadrosaurid from the latest Cretaceous of
North America. It was a contemporary of
Tyrannosaurus (see pp. 196–197) and
almost certainly fell prey to it on many
occasions.

It was a crestless hadrosaurid with a long,
flattened skull. Its beak was very broad,
and particularly duck-like. Far from being
used to dabble in ponds, its broad beak,

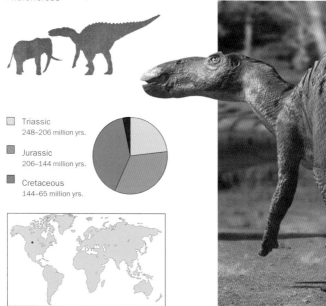

☐ Triassic
248–206 million yrs.

☐ Jurassic
206–144 million yrs.

☐ Cretaceous
144–65 million yrs.

FAMILY HADROSAURIDAE (IGUANODONTIA)

with its sharp cutting edge would have been used for cropping large amounts of low growing vegetation. Modern grazing herbivores also have broad mouths for cropping a lot of food in each mouthful. A mummified *Anatotitan*, with the contents of its stomach preserved, proved that it fed on land plants.

Like other hadrosaurids, *Anatotitan* had a deep flattened tail. This tail looks like a good sculling organ for an aquatic animal but close examination sows that it was poorly muscled and was held stiff by a lattice of bony tendons. Thus the deep tail may have been a display organ, or possibly a fat storage area.

ID FACT FILE

LENGTH:
9 m (30 ft)

WEIGHT:
4 tons

TIME:
Late Cretaceous

CLASSIFICATION:
Ornithischia
Neornithischia
Ornithopoda
Iguanodontia

DESCRIPTION:
Long head with broad beak and a small pointed crest above eyes. Body the same as Gryposaurus.

DIET:
Herbivorous

Maiasaura

(mother lizard)

Maisaura was a hadrosaurid that lived on the upper coastal plain of western North America in the Late Cretaceous. We know more about the biology of this dinosaur, than almost any other, thanks to a series of remarkable discoveries by palaeontologist John Horner. One of these discoveries was a nesting ground, complete with eggs and babies.

Many *Maiasaura* congregated to build scooped-out mounds of mud into which they laid their eggs. We know from the

Triassic
248–206 million yrs.

Jurassic
206–144 million yrs.

Cretaceous
144–65 million yrs.

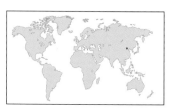

baby bones buried in these mounds that the young
stayed in the nest while the parents bought food to
them. This parental care can be proved by the fact
that the baby skeletons in the nest were 2–3 times as
big as the eggs, and so must have grown in the nest
for a certain period after hatching.

Another staggering discovery was a bonebed produced
when a massive herd, estimated to have contained
10,000 *Maiasaura*, was killed by a volcanic eruption.
It seems that *Maisaura* may have migrated annually
in herds along the upper coastal plain. Apart from
this it was a relatively plain looking solid-crested
hadrosaurid whose crest was a simple low ridge
above its eyes.

ID FACT FILE

LENGTH:
11 m (36 ft)

WEIGHT:
5.5 tons

TIME:
Late Cretaceous

CLASSIFICATION:
Ornithischia
Neornithischia
Ornithopoda
Iguanodontia

DESCRIPTION:
Long head with broad beak. Long pointed spike projecting backwards from between the eyes. Body the same as *Gryposaurus*.

DIET:
Herbivorous

Saurolophus
(lizard crest)

Saurolophus was one of the solid-crested hadrosaurids, which were as *Anatotitan* (see pp. 162–163) and Gryposaurus (see pp. 160–161).

In *Saurolophus* a solid, bony, spike projected up, and back, from the top of the head. The depressions that surround the bony nostrils of the skull extend up onto this spike suggesting that in life it supported an enlarged nasal chamber.

■ Triassic
248–206 million yrs.

■ Jurassic
206–144 million yrs.

■ Cretaceous
144–65 million yrs.

Perhaps this chamber formed an inflatable sac, that, when blown up, could act as a resonating chamber that would produce a very load call.

Saurolophus is interesting as it is found in both Western North America and Eastern Asia. This distribution provides evidence that a land-bridge across the Bering Sea existed at some point in the Late Cretaceous, allow animal to cross from one continent to the other. In Asia it would have formed the main food source of the tyrannosaurid, *Tarbosaurus* (see pp. 194–195).

ID FACT FILE

LENGTH:
9 m (30 ft)

WEIGHT:
4 tons

TIME:
Late Cretaceous

CLASSIFICATION:
Ornithischia
Neornithischia
Ornithopoda
Iguanodontia

DESCRIPTION:
Short deep head with narrow beak. Long thick, tube-like crest curving over neck from the back of the head. Body deep. Back bends strongly downwards towards the neck. Tall, fleshy ridge on top of back and tail.

DIET:
Herbivorous

Triassic
248–206 million yrs.

Jurassic
206–144 million yrs.

Cretaceous
144–65 million yrs.

Parasaurolophus
(beside Saurolophus)

Parasaurolophus was a member of the second major group of hadrosaurids: the hollow crested forms. As the name suggests the head crests of the hadrosaurids were hollowed out by large, tortuous nasal passages. A number of functions have been suggested for these but the only idea that seems feasible was that they were used as resonating chambers to produce a distinctive call (like the pipes of a trombone). Such calls would have

been very useful for social interactions and there is
ample evidence that hadrosaurids were herding
creatures.

Its crest was a large cylindrical structure, extending
back over the neck that could exceed in length the
rest of the head. Some specimens have a much shorter
and tightly curved crest, these may well have been
females. Hollow crested hadrosaurids had particularly
long, robust forelimbs and probably walked on four
legs for most of the time.

ID FACT FILE

LENGTH:
10 m (33 ft)

TIME:
Late Cretaceous

CLASSIFICATION:
Ornithischia
Neornithischia
Ornithopoda
Iguanodontia

DESCRIPTION:
As in
Parasaurolophus
except with a
semi-circular
plate-like crest
on top of the
head. Ribbon-like
skin frill on the
back and tail.

DIET:
Herbivorous

Corythosaurus

(helmeted lizard)

The hollow crest of *Corythosaurus* formed a large rounded crest over the top of its head which in profile resembled a helmet, hence the name. Like other hollow crested forms the crest appears to have varied between the sexes with the probable females having a smaller narrow crest than the males. Hatchlings of a close relative, *Hypacrosaurus*, show that the young had no crest and that it developed as the animal got older.

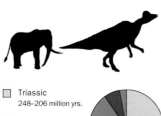

☐ Triassic
248–206 million yrs.

☐ Jurassic
206–144 million yrs.

☐ Cretaceous
144–65 million yrs.

FAMILY HADROSAURIDAE (IGUANODONTIA)

Another feature in common with other hollow crested hadrosaurids is the relatively narrow beak compared to those of crestless, and solid crested, hadrosaurids. This indicates that these animals were more choosy feeders probably plucking at the more nutritious leaves, rather than biting off large swathes of vegetation with each bite.

Excellent skin impressions have been found surrounding a *Corythosaurus* skeleton. These show that the skin was covered in a mosaic of large polygonal scales, and that there was a soft frill extending along the length of the back and tail.

ID FACT FILE

LENGTH:
15 m (50 ft)

TIME:
Late Cretaceous

CLASSIFICATION:
Ornithischia
Neornithischia
Ornithopoda
Iguanodontia

DESCRIPTION:
As in
Parasaurolophus
except with a
forward pointing
tongue-shaped
crest and a
backwards
pointing crest on
top of head.

DIET:
Herbivorous

Lambeosaurus

(Lambe's lizard)

Lambeosaurus was a hollow-crested hadrosaurid, closely related to *Corythosaurus*. It differed from that genus in having a tongue-shaped crest that leaned forward over the snout and a solid prong projecting back from the base of the crest.

Growth series of this dinosaur exist and show that the crest started out as a small bump in juveniles, which then enlarged as the animal grew.

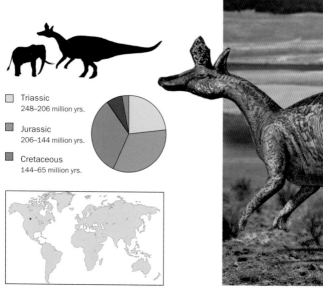

☐ Triassic
248–206 million yrs.

◪ Jurassic
206–144 million yrs.

◼ Cretaceous
144–65 million yrs.

FAMILY HADROSAURIDAE (IGUANODONTIA)

Female crests were not as large as those of the males. Thus it seems the external shape of the crest was an excellent marker of an individuals species, age and sex. Thus the crests would have played an important role in social interactions, which would have been important for these herd-forming dinosaurs.

All hollow-crested hadrosaurids had tall spines atop their vertebrae, which produced a tall ridge along their backs and a particularly deep tail. These features were especially well developed in *Lambeosaurus*.

ID FACT FILE

LENGTH:
10 m (33 ft)

WEIGHT:
7 tons

TIME:
Early Cretaceous

CLASSIFICATION:
Saurischia
Sauropodomorpha
Sauropoda
Neosauropoda

DESCRIPTION:
Large quadruped
with columnar
limbs. Head with
long low and wide
snout. Head
pointing down or
back. Moderately
long neck that is
bent downwards
Neck with 12
pairs of tall spines.
Forelimbs shorter
than hindlimbs.
High ridge over
back and tail.
Long tail.

DIET:
Herbivorous

☐ Triassic
248–206 million yrs.

▨ Jurassic
206–144 million yrs.

▨ Cretaceous
144–65 million yrs.

Amargasaurus

(lizard from La Amarga [Canyon])

It is becoming clear that the well-known
dinosaur faunas of the Cretaceous North
America and Asia were not typical of the
rest of the world. For instance we now
know that sauropods did not dwindle
towards extinction but continued to flourish
on other continents during the Cretaceous.

Amargasaurus was one of
these. It was related to
Diplodocus (see pp.
58–59), but looked very
different. Instead of
having a long, flexible
neck, its neck was shorter
and was bent steeply
downwards, so that the
head would have been
carried close to the ground.

FAMILY DICRAEOSAURIDAE (NEOSAUROPODA)

Thus it seems *Amargasurus* was a sauropod that
grazed upon the vegetation that covered the ground.
Adding to its bizarre appearance was a tall thick ridge
running over its back and hips. Most unusual of all,
were the pairs of long spines that projected from the
top of each vertebra of the neck. These spines
formed two parallel rows along the top of the neck.
The function of these spines remains unknown.

ID FACT FILE

LENGTH:
12 m (40 ft)

TIME:
Late Cretaceous

CLASSIFICATION:
Saurischia
Sauropodomorpha
Sauropoda
Neosauropoda

DESCRIPTION:
Body unknown,
almost certainly a
large quadruped
with columnar
limbs and a long
neck. Head long,
low and broad.
Nostrils above
eyes. Pencil
shaped teeth at
front of jaws only.

DIET:
Herbivorous

Nemegtosaurus

(lizard from the Nemegt)

Most sauropod skeletons are found without a skull because the small delicate head is easily destroyed by erosion or scavenging.

Nemegtosaurus is the complete opposite it is only known from an isolated skull. It also comes from a time and place where sauropods are rare and poorly known, making it very difficult to determine what kind of sauropod it really was.

- Triassic
  248–206 million yrs.

- Jurassic
  206–144 million yrs.

- Cretaceous
  144–65 million yrs.

FAMILY TITANOSAURIDAE (?) (NEOSAUROPODA)

The skull broadly resembles that of *Diplodocus* (see pp. 58–59) especially with its peg-like teeth restricted to the very front of its jaws. However, it is known that titanosaurids (eg. *Saltasaurus*, pp. 178–179) have evolved peg-like teeth as a convergence with diplodocids, and some of the features of *Nemegtosaurus* are titanosaurid-like.

If *Nemegtosaurus* really is a titanosaurid then it might belong to the headless titanosaurid skeleton called *Opisthocoelocaudia* (the name is quite a mouthful!) known from the same rock formation. The reconstruction presented here is based on this idea.

ID FACT FILE

LENGTH:
12 m (40 ft)

TIME:
Late Cretaceous

CLASSIFICATION:
Saurischia
Sauropodomorpha
Sauropoda
Neosauropoda

DESCRIPTION:
Heavy bodied
quadruped with
columnar limbs.
Moderately long
neck. Wide barrel-
shaped body with
level back.
Armoured with
large keeled
plates and
smaller studs.
Forefeet with no
toes or claws.
Hindfeet with five
toes and three
claws.

DIET:
Herbivorous

■ Triassic
248–206 million yrs.

■ Jurassic
206–144 million yrs.

■ Cretaceous
144–65 million yrs.

Saltasaurus

(lizard from Salta)

Saltasaurus was a typical Late
Cretaceous titanosaurid. These
sauropods were the dominant large
herbivores of the time in most parts of
the world, except North America and
Asia.

Titanosaurids can be recognized by their
unusual ball and socket joints between their
tail vertebrae. Despite their abundance,
titanosaurid fossils are frustratingly
incomplete. Their relationships have been

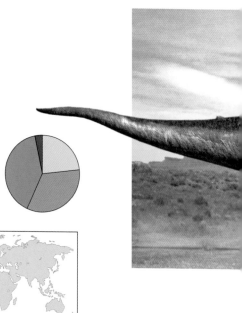

FAMILY TITANOSAURIDAE (NEOSAUROPODA)

obscure, partly because they display a mix of
Diplodocus-like and *Brachiosaurus*-like features.

It now seems likely that they were relatives of
Brachiosaurus (see pp. 64–65), which developed
some convergences with diplodocids (such as peg-like
teeth). Titanosaurids were quite variable and some
were amongst the largest of land animals, while
others were the smallest of all sauropods. While some
had armoured skin, others did not. *Saltasaurus* was
small with a heavily armoured, wide body. Its back
and sides were covered in small rounded studs, with
scattered larger keeled plates (approximately 10 cm
(4 in) in diameter).

FAMILY ABELISAURIDAE (CERATOSAURIA)

Carnotaurus

(flesh [-eating] bull)

ID FACT FILE

LENGTH:
7.5 m (24½ ft)

WEIGHT:
1 ton

TIME:
Late Cretaceous

CLASSIFICATION:
Saurischia
Theropoda
Ceratosauria

DESCRIPTION:
Large, but slender
biped. Head short
and deep. Large
triangular horn
over each eye.
Short thick neck.
Tiny arms with
very short forearm.
Hand with three
stubby fingers
and a spike.
Long legs with
three large toes
and a reduced
inner toe. Long
thick flexible tail.

DIET:
Carnivorous

This unusual looking theropod is perhaps
the best-preserved member of the recently
recognized abelisaurid family. As dinosaur
exploration outside of North America
improves, we are realising that abelisaurids
were the dominant large carnivores of
the latest Cretaceous in South America,
Africa, Madagascar, India and maybe
even Europe.
Abelisaurids are
characterized by
their unusual
vertebrae and
their short
snouts.

◻ Triassic
248–206 million yrs.

◼ Jurassic
206–144 million yrs.

◼ Cretaceous
144–65 million yrs.

Other unusual features of *Carnotaurus* are the two stout horns above its eyes and the extreme reduction of the arm bones below the elbow. Indeed these are so short as to give the appearance that the hand grew straight out of the elbow, without any forearm at all!

The hand also bore a large spike, somewhat like the thumbspike of *Iguanodon* (see pp. 156–157). The skeleton of *Carnotaurus* was preserved with skin impressions showing that it was covered with small round scales and larger conical studs.

ID FACT FILE

LENGTH:
9 m (30 ft)

TIME:
Late Cretaceous

CLASSIFICATION:
Saurischia
Theropoda
Ceratosauria

DESCRIPTION:
Like *Carnotaurus*
but with a tall
bump between
the eyes and no
horns.

DIET:
Carnivorous

Majungatholus

(dome from Majunga)

The first known fossil of this dinosaur was
just a piece of skull roof found on the island
of Madagascar. It was very thick and bulged
upwards into a tall mound-like structure
that closely resembled the domes that
adorned the heads of pachycephalosaurs
and so it was classified as one. But that
made it a fossil out of place because all
other domed pachycephalosaur fossils are
from the Late Cretaceous of
North America and Asia.

☐ Triassic
248–206 million yrs.

☐ Jurassic
206–144 million yrs.

☐ Cretaceous
144–65 million yrs.

FAMILY ABELISAURIDAE (CERATOSAURIA)

Majungatholus implied that this group was widespread
in the Jurassic, before the northern and southern
continents had separated. However no scrap of
these Jurassic pachycephalosaurs had ever been
found. The puzzle was solved when a complete skull
was found. It turned out that the 'dome' was actually
a short, stout horn growing out of a much larger
theropod skull. *Majungatholus* was a close relative
of *Carnotaurus* (see pp. 180–181) and like it had a
deep head with a short snout.

ID FACT FILE

LENGTH:
11 m (36 ft)

WEIGHT:
4 tons

TIME:
Early Cretaceous

CLASSIFICATION:
Saurischia
Theropoda
Tetanurae

DESCRIPTION:
Large heavy-bodied
biped. Head long
and low. Tip of
jaws expanded.
Small central
crest on snot in
front of eyes. Low
ridge on the back,
over the hips. Arms
large and thick.
Three fingers with
sharp claws.
Thumbclaw very
large. Three large
toes and a
reduced inner
toe on feet.

DIET:
Carnivorous, fish

Baryonyx
(heavy claw)

The discovery of *Baryonyx* within the
limits of Greater London in 1984
demonstrated that there still remains many
dinosaurs to be discovered even in such
densely inhabited and thoroughly searched
places as England.

The first bone to be found was a very
large curved claw, which suggested that
the animal could have been a giant
dromaeosaurid (eg. *Utahraptor*, see
pp. 218–219).

■ Triassic
248–206 million yrs.

■ Jurassic
206–144 million yrs.

■ Cretaceous
144–65 million yrs.

FAMILY SPINOSAURIDAE (TETANURAE)

However it turned out to be the thumb claw of an animal quite unlike any dromaeosaurid. The skull was long and low with an expanded tip (reminiscent of a crocodile) and the lower jaws were crowded with twice as many teeth as would be expected in a theropod of similar size.

We now think that *Baryonyx* was part of an unusual family of theropods, the Spinosauridae, which preyed upon fish. The crocodile-like jaws and teeth support the fish-eating hypothesis as does the remains of a large fish found in the stomach region of the skeleton of *Baryonyx*.

FAMILY SPINOSAURIDAE (TETANURAE)

ID FACT FILE

LENGTH:
7 m (23 ft)

TIME:
Early Cretaceous

CLASSIFICATION:
Saurischia
Theropoda
Tetanurae

DESCRIPTION:
Long low head
with widely
spaced straight
teeth. Snout-tip
may have had a
crest. Body
unknown but
probably bipedal.

DIET:
Carnivorous, fish

Irritator

(the irritating one)

Irritator received its unusual name when
the scientists who were studying it
discovered that its odd shape was partly
due to the specimen being doctored.
The collector of the specimen had used
fragments of bone and car body filler to
artificially lengthen the snout. This was
done to increase the commercial value of
the skull.

Triassic
248–206 million yrs.

Jurassic
206–144 million yrs.

Cretaceous
144–65 million yrs.

FAMILY SPINOSAURIDAE (TETANURAE)

Nevertheless, when the damage was repaired and the
fake parts removed, an extraordinary theropod skull
remained. Its snout was long and low with widely
spaced teeth. These teeth are quite unlike most other
theropods because they are straight, circular in cross-
section and lack serrations. The only other theropod
known to have teeth like these is the gigantic but poorly
known *Spinosaurus* from Africa. The skull shape is also
similar to other spinosaurids. A spinosaurid snout-tip
from the same locality as *Irritator* may belong to
this genus, if so it had a short crest at the front of its
snout.

FAMILY ALLOSAURIDAE (CARNOSAURIA)

ID FACT FILE

LENGTH:
10 m (33 ft)

WEIGHT:
3.5 tons

TIME:
Early Cretaceous

CLASSIFICATION:
Saurischia
Theropoda
Tetanurae
Carnosauria

DESCRIPTION:
Large heavy-bodied biped. Large deep head and a short thick neck. Low ridges on each side of the dorsal margin of the snout. Arms short. Three fingers with sharp claws. Strong legs with three main toes and a reduced inner toe.

DIET:
Carnivorous, large dinosaurs.

☐ Triassic
248–206 million yrs.

■ Jurassic
206–144 million yrs.

■ Cretaceous
144–65 million yrs.

Acrocanthosaurus

(high spined lizard)

Acrocanthosaurus was the largest terrestrial predator of the Early Cretaceous of North America. It was a carnosaur related to *Allosaurus* (see pp. 80–81). Like *Allosaurus* it only had three fingers in each hand, an advanced feature evolved convergently with coelurosaurs.

It differed from *Allosaurus* in having a low ridge instead of a triangular horn in front of

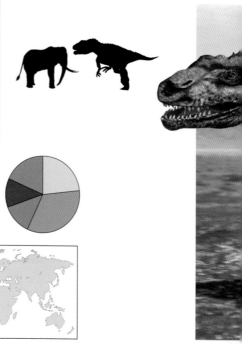

FAMILY ALLOSAURIDAE (CARNOSAURIA)

each eye. It also had very tall spines on top of each vertebra, producing a tall thick ridge that ran the full length of the spinal column, from behind the head to the end of the tail. The purpose of this ridge is unknown it may have supported a long, low hump.

Acrocanthosaurus probably preyed upon sauropods. A set of trackways preserved in the famous Palauxy River area of Texas shows a carnosaur (probably *Acrocanthosaurus*) following and attacking a sauropod. Unfortunately the trackway does not record the conclusion of this encounter.

ID FACT FILE

LENGTH:
12 m (40 ft)

WEIGHT:
6 tons

TIME:
Late Cretaceous

CLASSIFICATION:
Saurischia
Theropoda
Tetanurae
Carnosauria

DESCRIPTION:
Like *Acrocanthosaurus* but without a thick ridge along the neck, back and tail.

DIET:
Carnivorous, large dinosaurs.

Charcarodontosaurus
(shark-toothed lizard)

This was the last and amongst the largest of all carnosaurs. Although carnosaurs were the dominant large predators of the Jurassic and Early Cretaceous, they had died out by the end of the age of dinosaurs being replaced by tyrannosaurid coelurosaurs in the Northern Hemisphere and abelisaurid ceratosaurs in the Southern Hemisphere.

Although *Charcarodontosaurus* was very big, it is hard to say if it was actually the

☐ Triassic
248–206 million yrs.

☐ Jurassic
206–144 million yrs.

☐ Cretaceous
144–65 million yrs.

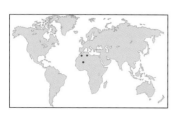

FAMILY CHARCARODONTOSAURIDAE (CARNOSAURIA)

biggest of all carnivorous dinosaurs without more complete remains. A close relative from South America, *Giganotosaurus*, and *Tyrannosaurus* also reached a similar size.

It is more interesting to recognize that theropods do not seem to have got any larger (as far as we know) so we may be looking at the absolute size limit for a theropod dinosaur. Apart from its larger size *Charcarodontosaurus* differed from other carnosaurs, like *Allosaurus* (see pp. 80–81), in having a narrower head without small horns in front of the eyes, and in having broad, triangular, shark-like teeth.

ID FACT FILE

LENGTH:
6 m (20 ft)

WEIGHT:
700 kg (1,543 lb)

TIME:
Late Cretaceous

CLASSIFICATION:
Saurischia
Theropoda
Coelurosauria

DESCRIPTION:
Medium sized
biped. Large head.
Snout with row of
six small horns.
Small forearms.
Number of fingers
unknown. Long
slender legs.
Three large toes
and a reduced
inner toe.

DIET:
Carnivorous

Alioramus

(other branch)

Alioramus was a primitive member of
the tyrannosaurid family. Unlike most
coelurosaurs, tyrannosaurids grew very
big and preyed on the largest herbivorous
dinosaurs in their habitat. Tyrannosaurs
became the dominant carnivores of North
America and Asia, replacing the carnosaurs
and abelisaurids that were the dominant
large carnivores elsewhere in the world.
Unlike the carnosaurs they have been
confused with in the past, tyrannosaurids
had slender hind legs with proportions
designed for fast running.

☐ Triassic
248–206 million yrs.

◼ Jurassic
206–144 million yrs.

◼ Cretaceous
144–65 million yrs.

FAMILY TYRANNOSAURIDAE (COELUROSAURIA)

They would have been the fastest animals alive, in their size range. Later tyrannosaurids developed deep, heavily-built skulls whereas *Alioramus* had a longer skull with weaker jaws that are more typical of other coelurosaurs.

Alioramus also differed from other tyrannosaurids in having a row of little spikes along its snout. It is not known whether Alioramus had three fingers like its coelurosaurian ancestors or if it had developed the two-fingered hand that characterizes later tyrannosaurids.

ID FACT FILE

LENGTH:
10 m (33 ft)

WEIGHT:
5 tons

TIME:
Late Cretaceous

CLASSIFICATION:
Saurischia
Theropoda
Tetanurae
Coelurosauria

DESCRIPTION:
Large biped.
Head large and
deep. Large thick
teeth. Neck short
and powerful.
Arms tiny with
only two fingers.
Long hind legs
with three large
toes and a small
inner toe. Tail
moderately long
with a stiff tip.

DIET:
Carnivorous,
large dinosaurs.

Tarbosaurus

(alarming lizard)

Tarbosaurus was the Asian equivalent
of *Tyrannosaurus* (see pp. 196–197).
Indeed it is so similar that some
argue that it is just a population of
Tyrannosaurus that was connected to the
North American population by a land
bridge through the Bering Strait that
probably existed in the latest Cretaceous.

Others argue that the similarities are due
to convergence and that *Tyrannosaurus* is
more closely related to earlier North
American tyrannosaurids and

☐ Triassic
248–206 million yrs.

☐ Jurassic
206–144 million yrs.

☐ Cretaceous
144–65 million yrs.

FAMILY TYRANNOSAURIDAE (COELUROSAURIA)

Tarbosaurus is more closely related to other
Asian tyrannosaurids, such as Alioramus (see
pp. 192–193).

Like *Tyrannosaurus*, *Tarbosaurus* had a large heavy
skull armed with big thick teeth and very reduced
arms with only two digits. It differed from
Tyrannosaurus in having 15 teeth in each lower jaw
(versus 14–13 for *Tyrannosaurus*) and in having a
skull that was narrower across the cheeks.

Tarbosaurus would have preyed upon the large
hadrosaurids, such as *Saurolophus*, that shared its
habitat.

ID FACT FILE

LENGTH:
12 m (40 ft)

WEIGHT:
6.7 tons

TIME:
Late Cretaceous

CLASSIFICATION:
Saurischia
Theropoda
Tetanurae
Coelurosauria

DESCRIPTION:
Large biped.
Head large and
deep. Cheek
region broad.
Large thick teeth.
Neck short and
powerful. Arms tiny
with only two
fingers. Long hind
legs with three
large toes and
small inner toe.
Tail moderately
long with a stiff tip.

DIET:
Carnivorous,
large dinosaurs.

Tyrannosaurus
(tyrant lizard)

This coelurosaur was close to, if not equal in size, to the largest carnosaurs but had a bulkier build and longer legs. Indeed the proportions of the hindlegs are those of a giant running animal. Although its top speed may not have exceeded 40 km/h (25 mph) (a trip or fall at higher speeds would have been fatal for such a giant), it was certainly the fastest animal of its size. It could have easily run down large hadrosaurids and ceratopsians.

☐ Triassic
   248–206 million yrs.

▨ Jurassic
   206–144 million yrs.

■ Cretaceous
   144–65 million yrs.

FAMILY TYRANNOSAURIDAE (COELUROSAURIA)

Studies of its teeth have revealed that the design of
the serrations on its teeth would have trapped fibres
of meat during feeding. These fibres would have
provided food for a legion of dangerous bacteria.
Thus most animals that escaped an attack from
Tyrannosaurus would, nevertheless, be killed by a
massive infection within days.

CAT scans of its brain cavity reveal that it had an
excellent sense of smell that could help it track such
dying prey.

FAMILY TYRANNOSAURIDAE (COELUROSAURIA)

ID FACT FILE

LENGTH:
5 m (16½ ft)

TIME:
Late Cretaceous

CLASSIFICATION:
Saurischia
Theropoda
Tetanurae
Coelurosauria

DESCRIPTION:
Large biped.
Head large and
deep. Cheek
region broad.
Large thick teeth.
Neck short and
powerful. Arms tiny
with only two
fingers. Long hind
legs with three
large toes and
small inner toe.
Tail moderately
long with a stiff tip.

DIET:
Carnivorous,
large dinosaurs.

Juvenile Tyrannosaurus
(tyrant lizard)

A small tyrannosaurid skull found in the same strata that produce *Tyrannosaurus* has been described as a pygmy tyrannosaurid, '*Nannotyrannus*'. It was thought to differ from *Tyrannosaurus* in having a longer, more pointed snout and more blade-shaped teeth.

Description of the growth stages of other tyrannosaurid genera has shown that a long pointed snout is a juvenile characteristic. Indeed an examination of the

☐ Triassic
248–206 million yrs.

☐ Jurassic
206–144 million yrs.

☐ Cretaceous
144–65 million yrs.

'*Nannotyrannus*' skull has revealed a number of features, such as bone texture, that indicate it is a juvenile. Furthermore it shares some distinctive characters that are only found in *Tyrannosaurus* such as a broad cheek region and small midline crest on the bones between the eyes (this would not have been visible in life). Thus most palaeontologist now accept that *Nannotyrannus* is a juvenile *Tyrannosaurus*.

The difference in the teeth suggests that juveniles sliced off meaty parts of a carcass while adults chewed through the whole thing – bones and all.

FAMILY ORNITHOMIMIDAE (COELUROSAURIA)

ID FACT FILE

LENGTH:
2 m (6½ ft)

TIME:
Early Cretaceous

CLASSIFICATION:
Saurischia
Theropoda
Tetanurae
Coelurosauria

DESCRIPTION:
Long slender neck
and small head
with pointed beak
and a throat
pouch. Small
fleshy crest
behind head.
Forearms long.
Three equal-sized
fingers with long,
straight claws.
Hindquarters
unknown. Skin
smooth.

DIET:
Unknown

Pelecanimimus
(pelican mimic)

Pelecanimimus is the earliest known
member of the ornithomimid family, which
are commonly called the ostrich-mimics.
They resemble ostriches in their long,
slender necks, small heads with pointed
beaks and long slim legs adapted for fast
running. Most ornithomimids lack any
teeth increasing their resemblance to
birds. In contrast *Pelecanimimus* had more teeth than any
other theropod.

□ Triassic
248–206 million yrs.

■ Jurassic
206–144 million yrs.

■ Cretaceous
144–65 million yrs.

FAMILY ORNITHOMIMIDAE (COELUROSAURIA)

Its teeth were tiny and closely packed so that together they formed a single cutting edge. Perhaps later ornithomimids swapped their teeth for sharp cutting edges on their horny beaks.

Various soft tissues were preserved along with the skeleton of *Pelecanimimus*. These show that there was a small soft crest at the back of the head and that there was a throat pouch, a bit like a pelican's, below its lower jaws. It had a wrinkled, naked skin that lacked both scales and feathers.

FAMILY ORNITHOMIMIDAE (COELUROSAURIA)

ID FACT FILE

LENGTH:
4 m (13 ft)

WEIGHT:
150 kg (330 lb)

TIME:
Late Cretaceous

CLASSIFICATION:
Saurischia
Theropoda
Tetanurae
Coelurosauria

DESCRIPTION:
Small head.
Pointed
toothless beak.
Neck long and
slender.
Compact body.
Forearms long.
Three equal-sized
fingers with long,
straight claws.
Long legs.
Three toes with
blunt claws.
Moderately long
tail with stiff tip.

DIET:
Herbivorous

☐ Triassic
248–206 million yrs.

☐ Jurassic
206–144 million yrs.

☐ Cretaceous
144–65 million yrs.

Struthiomimus

(ostrich mimic)

Struthiomimus was a typical Late
Cretaceous ornithomimid. It had small
head with a pointed, toothless beak and
elongated lower legs that were well
adapted for fast running. Like all toothless
ornithomimids it was probably a herbivore.

Its forelimbs had many peculiarities that
it shared with other members of its
family. The claws on its fingers were long

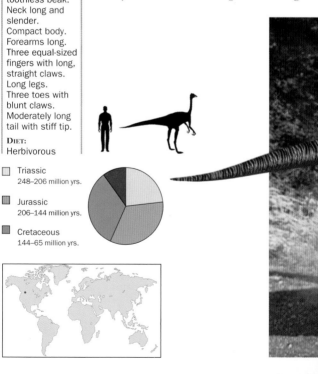

and straight, unlike the strongly-curved claws of most other theropods. Such claws were not effective for grasping prey.

Another peculiarity was the thumb, which did not oppose the other fingers as it does in most other theropods. Instead it moved in parallel with the other fingers. This reduced its grasping ability even further but caused the whole, narrow hand to form a hook-like structure when flexed. Perhaps this hook was used to pull down branches of trees so that the animal could browse on them.

ID FACT FILE

LENGTH:
6 m (20 ft)

WEIGHT:
600 kg (1,323 lb)

TIME:
Late Cretaceous

CLASSIFICATION:
Saurischia
Theropoda
Tetanurae
Coelurosauria

DESCRIPTION:
Same as
Struthiomimus,
only with a
blunter snout tip
and shorter
hands.

DIET:
Herbivorous

Gallimimus

(chicken mimic)

This was a large Asian ornithomimid. It was closely related to *Struthiomimus* (see pp. 202–203) and looked quite similar to it. The main differences were that the beak had a blunter tip and that the hands were shorter. This could have meant that *Gallimimus* had less of a reach and therefore, did not browse from tall trees as often as *Struthiomimus* did.

Triassic
248–206 million yrs.

Jurassic
206–144 million yrs.

Cretaceous
144–65 million yrs.

FAMILY ORNITHOMIMIDAE (COELUROSAURIA)

Related ornithomimid remains from China show that they were herbivores that plucked food with their beaks then ground it up in a gizzard filled with grit and small pebbles.

Like other ornithomimids the foot of *Gallimimus* was adapted to little else but fast running. The inner toe was completely missing and the remaining toes were short and their claws very blunt. Juvenile *Gallimimus* skulls have been found. These had larger eyes and shorter beaks than the adults.

FAMILY ALXASAURIDAE (COELUROSAURIA)

ID FACT FILE

LENGTH:
4 m (13 ft)

WEIGHT:
200 kg (440 lb)

TIME:
Early Cretaceous

CLASSIFICATION:
Saurischia
Theropoda
Tetanurae
Coelurosauria

DESCRIPTION:
Heavy bodied
biped. Head small
and neck long.
Arms long. Hand
with three fingers
each with a large
curved claw. Foot
with four toes.
Tail short.

DIET:
Herbivorous

Alxasaurus

(lizard from the Alxa Desert)

The discovery of *Alxasaurus* was like the dinosaurian equivalent of finding the Rosetta Stone, because it cleared up a number of mysteries at once. The first puzzle it solved was the proper placement of the weird segnosaurs.

Alxasaurus was clearly a member of this group as it had the same down-turned jaws, leaf-like teeth and four-toed foot with long straight claws that

Triassic
248–206 million yrs.

Jurassic
206–144 million yrs.

Cretaceous
144–65 million yrs.

other segnosaurs had. Segnosaurs were once thought of as late surviving prosauropods or possibly primitive ornithischians. However *Alxasaurus* was complete enough to show that they were clearly theropods related to *Oviraptor* (see pp. 212–213).

Alxasaurus also showed us for the first time what the skeleton of a segnosaur looked like. They were fat-bodied, large-armed and short-tailed bipeds. The structure of the hand of *Alxasaurus* also solved the identity of some mystery hands that had been called

Therizinosaurus (see pp. 208–209). Many similarities between the two such as the unusually large and straight claws showed that *Therizinosaurus* was a very large segnosaur.

Therizinosaurus

(scythe lizard)

This dinosaur had astonishing sword-like claws on its hands. When these were first found they were thought to be from some kind of gigantic turtle. Later on their dinosaur affinities were recognized, and later still palaeontologists realized that it was a very large segnosaur. None of these later segnosaurs are known from complete remains so the reconstruction seen here is based on a combination of different large segnosaur parts from the Late Cretaceous.

Triassic
248–206 million yrs.

Jurassic
206–144 million yrs.

Cretaceous
144–65 million yrs.

Their hips were broadly flared to support a massive, barrel-shaped gut. Large guts are needed to cope with nutrient-poor plant material. The head was small and ended in a toothless beak. Its hands bore the largest claws of any dinosaur. These claws may have been used in defence although it has been speculated that they were used to rip open termite nests.

It seems improbable that a multi-ton giant, like *Therizinosaurus*, was able to sustain itself on a diet of ants and termites.

ID FACT FILE

LENGTH:
90 cm (35 in)

TIME:
Early Cretaceous

CLASSIFICATION:
Saurischia
Theropoda
Tetanurae
Coelurosauria

DESCRIPTION:
Small, short skull with down turned jaw tips. Small cluster of teeth at the front of upper jaw. Neck long and slender. Short arm with three-fingered hand, Long legs with three main toes and reduced first toe. Very short tail. Body covered with downy feathers. Arms and tail with fans of long feathers.

DIET:
Herbivorous

Caudipteryx
(tail feather)

This animal provided the final clinching evidence that has more or less settled the question of origin of the birds. It was a small theropod related to the oviraptorids and was preserved with unquestionable feathers.

Fans of feathers grew from the second finger of the hand and from the tip of the tail. This was the first time that true feathers had been found with the skeleton of non-bird.

☐ Triassic
248–206 million yrs.

☐ Jurassic
206–144 million yrs.

☐ Cretaceous
144–65 million yrs.

FAMILY UNNAMED (COELUROSAURIA)

There are some palaeontologists who contend that it is a true, flightless bird. Nevertheless the close similarities between *Caudipteryx* and oviraptorids make this hypothesis unlikely.

Like oviraptorids, *Caudipteryx* has a short, deep skull, a toothless lower jaw with a bent-down tip, and a very short tail. Unlike true oviraptorids, however, it retained four small pointed teeth at the front of the upper jaws. Its 'wings' were far too small for flight so they may have been used for display.

FAMILY OVIRAPTORIDAE (COELUROSAURIA)

ID FACT FILE

LENGTH:
2.5 m (8 ft)

WEIGHT:
35 kg (77 lb)

TIME:
Late Cretaceous

CLASSIFICATION:
Saurischia
Theropoda
Tetanurae
Coelurosauria

DESCRIPTION:
Large deep head
decorated with a
tall crest. Jaws
toothless with a
horny beak. Long
arms. Hand with
three grasping
fingers and
curved claws.
Hind foot with
three main toes
and a reduced
first toe. Probably
with feathers.

DIET:
Herbivorous

Oviraptor
(egg thief)

Oviraptor was easily one of the strangest
theropods. Its toothless lower jaw had an
unusual joint with the upper jaw that
allowed it to slide back and forth. The
upper jaws were also toothless, save for
two bony projections arising
from the middle of the roof
of the mouth.

All these features
indicate that it had a
highly specialized diet

☐ Triassic
248–206 million yrs.

☐ Jurassic
206–144 million yrs.

☐ Cretaceous
144–65 million yrs.

FAMILY OVIRAPTORIDAE (COELUROSAURIA)

and feeding mechanism. Unfortunately we have little idea what this diet might have been. Its name suggests that it subsisted on a diet of other dinosaur's eggs. This was because the first skeleton was found lying on top of a nest of eggs. These eggs were once thought to belong to *Protoceratops* (see pp. 134–135), but since the discovery of an embryonic skeleton inside one of them we know that they are Oviraptor's own eggs. Its seems that the skeleton was that of the mother that died trying to protect her nest from the oncoming sandslide that buried it.

FAMILY OVIRAPTORIDAE (COELUROSAURIA)

ID FACT FILE

LENGTH:
1.8 m (6 ft)

TIME:
Late Cretaceous

CLASSIFICATION:
Saurischia
Theropoda
Tetanurae
Coelurosauria

DESCRIPTION:
Large deep head.
Jaws toothless
with a horny
beak. Long arms.
Hand with threes
stout fingers.
First finger (thumb)
is the largest.
Hind foot with
three main toes
and a reduced
first toe. Tail very
short. Probably
with feathers.

DIET:
Herbivorous

Ingenia

(from Ingen-[Khobur])

Ingenia was a close relative of *Oviraptor* (see pp. 212–213) and would have looked a lot like it but for two differences. The immediately obvious difference is that it lacked the tall head crest that adorned *Oviraptor*. The other difference lies in the hand. In *Oviraptor* the digits were long (with the middle finger being the longest) and adapted for grasping whereas those of *Ingenia* were short and stubby.

☐ Triassic
  248–206 million yrs.

☐ Jurassic
  206–144 million yrs.

☐ Cretaceous
  144–65 million yrs.

FAMILY OVIRAPTORIDAE (COELUROSAURIA)

The thumb was the longest and thickest digit
of the hand and bore a stout claw. The thumb of
Ingenia resembled the enlarged thumb of some
prosauropods, such as *Massospondylus* (see pp.
48–49), and, like these dinosaurs, probably used it
as a defensive weapon. *Ingenia* had the same strange
jaw specializations as *Oviraptor* and so would have
had a similar diet, whatever it was.

Some type of herbivory is possible given that the
related *Caudipteryx* (see pp. 210–211) had a stone-
filled gizzard for breaking down plant material.

Troodon

(wounding tooth)

ID FACT FILE

LENGTH:
3.5 m (11½ ft)

WEIGHT:
50 kg (110 lb)

TIME:
Late Cretaceous

CLASSIFICATION:
Saurischia
Theropoda
Tetanurae
Coelurosauria

DESCRIPTION:
Small lightly built
biped. Long low
head. Moderately
long neck. Long
arms and hands.
Three fingers
with sharp claws.
Long, slender
hindlimbs. Foot
with sharp
curved claw on
second toe.

DIET:
Carnivorous,
small vertebrates,
mammals.

Troodon was one of the first North
American dinosaurs to receive a name. At
the time only isolated teeth were known.
When other parts were found they were
given a different name. It took many
decades to match the teeth to the correct
skeleton.

Troodon had one of the largest brains of
any dinosaur. It also had large eyes and a
narrow snout filled with small, curved,
and coarsely serrated teeth, possibly

■ Triassic
248–206 million yrs.

■ Jurassic
206–144 million yrs.

■ Cretaceous
144–65 million yrs.

FAMILY TROODONTIDAE (COELUROSAURIA)

adaptations for preying on mammals. The foot had a large sickle-shaped claw on its second toe, that could be lifted off the ground while walking. This resembled a smaller version of the sickle-claw of dromaeosaurids (eg. *Deinonychus* and *Velociraptor* see pp. 218–225) and suggests that *Troodon* may be related to this family.

A *Troodon* has been found buried on top of a nest of eggs containing *Troodon* embryos which indicates some parental care took place after the eggs were laid.

ID FACT FILE

LENGTH:
6 m (20 ft)

WEIGHT:
700 kg (1,543 lb)

TIME:
Early Cretaceous

CLASSIFICATION:
Saurischia
Theropoda
Tetanurae
Coelurosauria

DESCRIPTION:
Medium sized
heavily built biped.
Large deep head.
Long arms.
Hands with large
blade-like claws.
Relatively short,
robust hindlegs.
Second toe with
very large, sharp
curved claw. Long
stiff tail. Probably
with feathers.

DIET:
Carnivorous,
other dinosaurs.

Utahraptor
(Utah thief)

Utahraptor was among the biggest of all
dromaeosaurids, the well-known theropod
family that are often (and incorrectly)
called 'raptors'.

A distinctive feature of dromaeosaurids
was their giant sickle-shaped claw that
grew on the second toe of their feet. This
claw was needle sharp at its
tip and had a blade-like
lower edge. The second toe
was designed so that the
claw could be pulled up off
the ground while walking so
that it remained sharp.

☐ Triassic
   248–206 million yrs.

☐ Jurassic
   206–144 million yrs.

☐ Cretaceous
   144–65 million yrs.

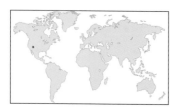

FAMILY DROMAEOSAURIDAE (COELUROSAURIA)

There is no doubt that such a fearsome weapon was used to dispatch prey, possibly using slashing kicks. The hand claws of *Utahraptor* were proportionately bigger and more blade-like than in other dromaeosaurids suggesting that they also played a big role in making a kill. *Utahraptor* lived at about the same time as the tiny *Microraptor* (see pp. 220–221), indicating that the family had already diversified greatly by this stage and hinting at a hidden history going back into the Jurassic.

ID FACT FILE

LENGTH:
45 cm (18 in)

WEIGHT:
300 g (11 oz)

TIME:
Early Cretaceous

CLASSIFICATION:
Saurischia
Theropoda
Tetanurae
Coelurosauria

DESCRIPTION:
Tiny biped. Short
triangular head.
Long arms.
Slender hindlegs.
Four toes with
curved sharp
claws. Inner toe
reduced. Second
toe with large claw.
Moderately long
stiff tail. Body
covered in long
downy feathers.

DIET:
Carnivorous,
insects, small
vertebrates.

Microraptor

(small thief)

Microraptor is another feathered dinosaur
from the Liaoning Province of China. It is
also the smallest known adult dinosaur
(not including birds, which are also
dinosaurs) beating *Compsognathus* (see
pp. 82–83) which has held this title for
well over 100 years.

Microraptor had a greatly enlarged,
sickle-shaped claw on the second toe of
the foot, and an inflexible tail stiffened by
bony rods as did other members of the
Dromaeosauridae.

☐ Triassic
248–206 million yrs.

▨ Jurassic
206–144 million yrs.

■ Cretaceous
144–65 million yrs.

FAMILY DROMAEOSAURIDAE (COELUROSAURIA)

The enlarged claw could have been used for killing prey or for climbing trees. The other claws were also sharp and strongly curved. It also had digit proportions similar to tree climbing animals. Thus *Microraptor* would have been more than capable of climbing up into trees (of course we may never know if it really did so).

So a dinosaurian origin of the birds need not imply a ground-up origin of flight. Birds could have evolved from a small arboreal coelurosaur like *Microraptor*.

ID FACT FILE

LENGTH:
3 m (10 ft)

WEIGHT:
45 kg (100 lb)

TIME:
Early Cretaceous

CLASSIFICATION:
Saurischia
Theropoda
Tetanurae
Coelurosauria

DESCRIPTION:
Long arms and
hands; three
fingers with sharp
curved claws.
Short, robust
legs; short
second toe with
large, retractable
claw. Long stiff
tail, probably
feathered.

DIET:
Carnivorous,
other dinosaurs.

☐ Triassic
248–206 million yrs.

☐ Jurassic
206–144 million yrs.

☐ Cretaceous
144–65 million yrs.

Deinonychus
(terrible claw)

Professor John Ostrom's study of this
dinosaur in 1969 did more than any other
work to spark the 'dinosaur renaissance'
of the late 20th century.

Previous views painted dinosaurs as slow,
cold-blooded creatures that went extinct
without leaving any descendants. Yet here
was an apparently agile predator. Its tail
was stiffened with numerous bony rods,
so that it formed a counterbalancing rod.
The reason it needed such a counter-
balance became obvious when the foot
was examined.

FAMILY DROMAEOSAURIDAE (COELUROSAURIA)

The claw of the second toe had become enlarged into a viciously sharp sickle-shaped weapon. To use this claw the animal would have had to have leapt up onto the animal and delivered a powerful kick, a feat that would require excellent balance.

The other surprise that was that many parts of the skeleton of *Deinonychus* were almost bone-for-bone matches with those of *Archaeopteryx* (see pp. 86–87), the earliest known bird. This revived the old idea that birds are the direct descendants of coelurosaurian dinosaurs.

FAMILY DROMAEOSAURIDAE (COELUROSAURIA)

ID FACT FILE

LENGTH:
2 m (6½ ft)

WEIGHT:
15 kg (33 lb)

TIME:
Late Cretaceous

CLASSIFICATION:
Saurischia
Theropoda
Tetanurae
Coelurosauria

DESCRIPTION:
Like *Deinonychus*
but head lower
profile of snout
depressed,
between nostrils
and eyes

DIET:
Carnivorous,
small dinosaurs
and other
vertebrates.

Velociraptor
(fast thief)

This is perhaps the best known of all
dromaeosaurids. It is known from many
superbly preserved skeletons from the
Gobi Desert of Asia. It was a small
dromaeosaurid that differed from others in
having a long low head with a distinctive
depression in the profile of the snout. It
lived in a sandy desert along with
Oviraptor (see pp. 212–213) and
Protoceratops (see pp. 134–135).

☐ Triassic
248–206 million yrs.

☐ Jurassic
206–144 million yrs.

☐ Cretaceous
144–65 million yrs.

FAMILY DROMAEOSAURIDAE (COELUROSAURIA)

Protoceratops may have been its main prey, indeed the skeleton of a *Velociraptor* has been found locked in what appears to be a fatal struggle with a *Protoceratops*.

Like other dromaeosaurids, *Velociraptor* shows many bird-like details in its skeleton such as a furcula (wishbone) in the shoulder girdle, large half-moon shaped bone in the wrist and a backswept pubic bone (the 'bird-hipped' condition). The proportions of the digits of the hands also match those of *Archaeopteryx* closely.

FAMILY HESPERORNITHIDAE (AVES)

ID FACT FILE

LENGTH:
2 m (6½ ft)

TIME:
Late Cretaceous

CLASSIFICATION:
Saurischia
Theropoda
Tetanurae
Coelurosauria
Aves

DESCRIPTION:
Large bird. Long
low head with
toothed beak.
Long neck. Tiny,
rudimentary wings.
Splayed hind legs
placed far back on
body. Four toes,
outer toes larger
than inner toes.
Tail reduced to
a stump.

DIET:
Fish

Hesperornis
(single crested lizard)

Hesperornis was an early toothed bird. It
had had given up its powers of flight to
become an aquatic fish hunter, much like
the modern penguin. It was so adapted
for this mode of life that its wings had
reduced to tiny splints of bone and it
could no longer walk upright on land.
Instead it would have to push itself along
on its belly. This was
because the legs were
placed very far back along
the long body and stuck
out sideways to gain

□ Triassic
   248–206 million yrs.

□ Jurassic
   206–144 million yrs.

□ Cretaceous
   144–65 million yrs.

FAMILY HESPERORNITHIDAE (AVES)

maximum propulsion from the kicks of its powerful webbed feet.

Like modern diving birds it has all of its toes rotated to point forwards. Its bones have been found in marine rocks that were hundreds if not thousands of kilometres from the nearest shoreline. Obviously this bird was used to travelling far out to sea. It probably spent most of its life at sea, returning to shore only to breed.

Ichthyornis

(fish bird)

Ichthyornis fossils have been found
alongside those of *Hesperornis* (see pp.
226–227), so it too was no stranger to the
open sea. However unlike *Hesperornis*,
it could fly. It had well developed wings
and a deeply keeled breastbone for the
attachment of flight muscles. Despite the
rather modern appearance of its flight
apparatus it still
retained teeth in

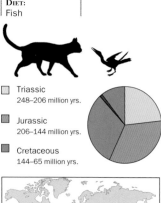

Triassic
248–206 million yrs.

Jurassic
206–144 million yrs.

Cretaceous
144–65 million yrs.

FAMILY ICHTHYORNITHIDAE (AVES)

its jaws. These teeth were small, curved and sharp and would have been very useful for holding onto slippery prey.

When it was first found the idea of a toothed bird was so bizarre that the jaws were identified as belonging to a small marine lizard despite the fact they were found together with the rest of the *Ichthyornis* skeleton. We now know that those jaws really did belong to *Ichthyornis*. It probably lived like a modern tern or gull, flying out to sea and plucking small fish from the surface of the water.

ID FACT FILE

LENGTH:
2.5 m (8 ft)

TIME:
Early Cretaceous

CLASSIFICATION:
Amphibia,
Temnospondyli

DESCRIPTION:
Large, sprawling
quadruped.
Large, flattened,
semicircular head.
Eyes directed
upwards. Mouth
with two rows of
sharp teeth and
several pairs of
fangs. Short
limbs, forefoot
with four toes,
hindfoot with
five. Tail shorter
than body.

DIET:
Carnivorous,
mostly fish.

Koolasuchus

(Kool's crocodile)

Koolasuchus is the last known member of the temnospondyls, a large group of amphibians that dominated the waterways of the world long before the dinosaurs evolved.

Most temnospondyls died out at the end of the Triassic but a few relatives of *Koolasuchus* survived past this boundary. *Koolasuchus* may have been able to survive for so long because it lived close to the South Pole, as did *Laellynasaura* (see pp. 150–151).

■ Triassic
248–206 million yrs.

■ Jurassic
206–144 million yrs.

■ Cretaceous
144–65 million yrs.

FAMILY CHIGUTISAURIDAE (TEMNOSPONDYLI)

Competitors such as crocodiles may not have been able to withstand the polar winters.

Koolasuchus was an aquatic animal as shown by the weak nature of its limb joints and vertebral column and the presence of a sensory canal system (like the lateral lines of a fish) impressed upon the bones of its skull. It was a predator that probably fed largely on fish it was capable of taking a small dinosaur while it drank at the water's edge.

ID FACT FILE

LENGTH:
11 m (36 ft)

TIME:
Late Cretaceous

CLASSIFICATION:
Reptilia
Diapsida
Plesiosauria

DESCRIPTION:
Large marine
reptile. Head tiny
with short snout.
Very long
interlocking
teeth. Neck
longer than the
rest of the body,
thin and flexible.
Short rounded
body. Paddle-like
limbs. Tail short.

DIET:
Carnivorous,
Fish.

Elasmosaurus
(thin-plated reptile)

Elasmosaurus and its relatives, represent
the extreme end of the long necked
plesiosaur body plan. In *Elasmosaurus*
the long, serpentine neck took up more
than half the length of the body. These
advanced plesiosaurs also reached very
large sizes, often exceeding 10 m (33 ft)
in length.

Their relatively tiny heads were
filled with very long interlocking
spiky teeth ideal for snagging
slippery prey such as fish.

Triassic
248–206 million yrs.

Jurassic
206–144 million yrs.

Cretaceous
144–65 million yrs.

FAMILY ELASMOSAURIDAE (PLESIOSAURIA)

The paddles of *Elasmosaurus* were proportionately smaller than in other plesiosaurs suggesting that it was a slower swimmer, relying on stealth rather than outright speed to capture its prey.

It may well have positioned itself near schools of fish and then thrust its small head into the middle of it, plucking prey with quick movements of its light head and flexible neck. This would result in a big catch for minimal effort.

FAMILY POLYCOTYLIDAE (PLESIOSAURIA)

ID FACT FILE

LENGTH:
10 m (33 ft)

TIME:
Early Cretaceous

CLASSIFICATION:
Reptilia
Diapsida
Plesiosauria

DESCRIPTION:
Large marine
reptile. Long, flat
head with
triangular snout.
Neck short and
thick. Body
compact. Limbs
form long paddles.
Tail short.

DIET:
Carnivorous,
large fish, other
marine reptiles.

Kronosaurus
(Kronos lizard)

The polycotylids, including *Kronosaurus*,
were big headed, short-necked predatory
plesiosaurs of the Cretaceous. Indeed the
length of their skulls exceeded the length
of their necks.

They looked a lot like the pliosaurs of the
Jurassic (see *Rhomaleosaurus*, pp. 96–97)
and are often classified as pliosaurs.

Nevertheless they share a
number of specialized
features with elasmosaurids

☐ Triassic
248–206 million yrs.

☐ Jurassic
206–144 million yrs.

☐ Cretaceous
144–65 million yrs.

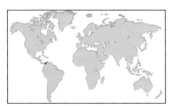

FAMILY POLYCOTYLIDAE (PLESIOSAURIA)

(eg. *Elasmosaurus* pp. 232–233), such as a reduction in the number of bones of the lower jaw. This indicates that they evolved a pliosaurid like body shape convergently with true pliosaurs.

Kronosaurus was one of the largest of all plesiosaurians. Its huge, flat, head was nearly 3 m (10 ft) long and was filled with pointed teeth the size of bananas. It was clearly a predator that could eat almost anything it came across. Likely prey items included large fish, turtles and elasmosaurids.

ID FACT FILE

LENGTH:
60 cm (24 in)

TIME:
Early Cretaceous

CLASSIFICATION:
Reptilia, Diapsida
Archosauria
Crurotarsi
Crocodyliformes

DESCRIPTION:
Tiny crocodylian,
with a long flat
snout. Several
rows of armour
plates on its back.

DIET:
Carnivorous,
fish, crustaceans
and other small
animals.

Bernissartia
(from Bernissart)

Bernissartia was closely related to the
ancestors of the modern Crocodylia.
Indeed, apart from its small adult size, it
would have looked little different from a
modern broad-snouted crocodile.
Nevertheless it is not included in the
group because it lacked certain specialized
features of the palate and vertebral column.

The remains of *Bernissartia* were found
alongside many complete *Iguanodon*

- ☐ Triassic
  248–206 million yrs.

- ☐ Jurassic
  206–144 million yrs.

- ☐ Cretaceous
  144–65 million yrs.

FAMILY BERNISSARTIIDAE (CROCODYLIFORMES)

(see pp. 156–157) skeletons in the famous coal mine of Bernissart, in Belgium.

Like modern crocodiles, *Bernissartia* would have been an amphibious animal, dwelling in lakes and rivers. Its jaws had pointed teeth at the front for catching and holding fast, slippery prey such as fish. The teeth at the rear of the jaw were thick and blunt, and were ideal for crushing hard-shelled prey such as crustaceans.

ID FACT FILE

WINGSPAN:
7 m (23 ft)

WEIGHT:
17 kg (37 lb)

TIME:
Late Cretaceous

CLASSIFICATION:
Reptilia, Diapsida
Archosauria
Ornithodira
Pterosauria
Pterodactyloidea

DESCRIPTION:
Large winged
reptile. Almost
tail-less. Long
narrow wings
supported by long
fourth finger.
Four toes. Head
long and low.
Jaws pointed and
toothless. Long
crest projecting
back from rear of
skull.

DIET:
Carnivorous,
fish.

☐ Triassic
   248–206 million yrs.

■ Jurassic
   206–144 million yrs.

■ Cretaceous
   144–65 million yrs.

Pteranodon
(winged, without teeth)

Pteranodon is perhaps the most familiar of the large, Late Cretaceous pterosaurs. Its long back-swept head crest produces a very recognizable profile.

Some have suggested that the crest may have acted as a rudder or as a stabilizer for the head during flight but both of these ideas seem unlikely. Not only were the crests quite variable between individuals (those with very small crests were probably female) but related

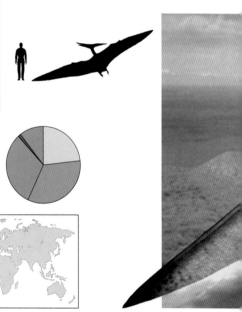

species were able to fly without any crest at all. It seems quite probable that these were display structures used to impress mates and intimidate rivals.

Its long pointed jaws had no teeth, it almost certainly plucked fish from the sea and swallowed them whole. Its remains are found buried in marine deposits that formed many hundreds of kilometres from the shore indicating that this pterosaur was used to long ocean flights. Indeed it may have spent most of its life at sea, as do some modern seabirds.

Anhanguera

(old devil)

The fossils of *Anhanguera* are some of
the best pterosaur fossils of all. Not only
are its skeletons complete, but the bones
have not been crushed flat by the weight
of overlying sediments (this usually
happens to delicate pterosaur bones).
What is more, some of its remains
include mineralized soft tissues such as
patches of skin and wing membrane.

The uncrushed pelvis of *Anhanguera* has
helped resolve the debate
centred upon the walking
posture of pterosaurs. Some
have said that they
walked erect on their
hind feet, while the wings
were folded up as modern
birds do, while others have

Triassic
248–206 million yrs.

Jurassic
206–144 million yrs.

Cretaceous
144–65 million yrs.

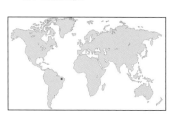

FAMILY ANHANGUERIDAE (PTERODACTYLOIDEA)

maintain that they were quadrupedal sprawlers, like modern bats. The hip sockets of *Anhanguera* show conclusively that it was impossible for it to bring its legs into the erect stance and that the latter model of locomotion must be the correct one.

The low crests above and below the jaw may have helped it cut water while fishing on the wing, or may have been used for display.

ID FACT FILE

WINGSPAN:
5 m (16½ ft)

TIME:
Early Cretaceous

CLASSIFICATION:
Reptilia, Diapsida
Archosauria
Ornithodira
Pterosauria
Pterodactyloidea

DESCRIPTION:
Large winged
reptile. Almost
tail-less. Short
broad wings
supported by long
fourth finger.
Head narrow and
deep. Toothless
pointed jaws.
Huge dorsal
head crest

DIET:
Carnivorous, fish
and aquatic
invertebrates.

Tapejara
(ancient being)

Tapejarids were pterodactyloid
pterosaurs that were closely related
to the giant azhdarchid family, which
includes *Quetzalcoatlus* (see pp.
244–245). Like them their small eyes
were placed low down on the sides of the
head. They also had short, broad wings
compared to other pterosaurs with the
shoulders placed very low on the flanks,
like a modern 'bottom-decker' plane.
Both of these features suggest that they
were slow but highly manoeuvrable fliers.

☐ Triassic
248–206 million yrs.

☐ Jurassic
206–144 million yrs.

☐ Cretaceous
144–65 million yrs.

FAMILY TAPEJARIDAE (PTERODACTYLOIDEA)

Unlike most pterosaurs, the skull of *Tapejara* was short and deep. The jaws were toothless and the tips protruded as pointed, forceps-like structures. The skull had two bony crests one on top of the head, in front of the eyes, the other projecting backwards from the rear of the head.

We know from spectacularly well preserved fossils that these crests formed the bases for a single, enormous, soft-tissue sail that whose height was about three times the length of the skull.

ID FACT FILE

WINGSPAN:
11 m (36 ft)

WEIGHT:
150 kg (330 lb)

TIME:
Late Cretaceous

CLASSIFICATION:
Reptilia, Diapsida
Archosauria
Ornithodira
Pterosauria
Pterodactyloidea

DESCRIPTION:
Giant winged
reptile. Almost
tail-less. Short
broad wings
supported by
fourth finger.
Neck long and
stiff. Beak long
and toothless.
Short crest on
top of head.

DIET:
Fish, and other
small animals.

Quetzalcoatlus

(named after Quetzalcoatl)

Quetzalcoatlus was amongst the last of
the pterosaurs and was quite possibly the
largest flying animal of all time. Indeed
the largest bones come from an animal
the size of a small aeroplane.

Its remains have been found in an inland
site that formed on a floodplain, so it
seems that the animal did not soar over
the open ocean in the manner that
Pteranodon did (see pp. 238–239).

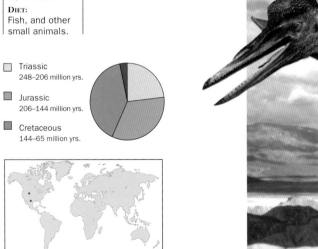

- ☐ Triassic
  248–206 million yrs.

- ☐ Jurassic
  206–144 million yrs.

- ☐ Cretaceous
  144–65 million yrs.

FAMILY AZHDARCHIDAE (PTERODACTYLOIDEA)

Some people have speculated that the animal lived like a giant vulture, riding thermal updrafts and using its long neck to probe dinosaur carcasses. However the skull was unknown, when this was proposed. We now know that it had a long straight toothless beak that was inappropriate for tearing carrion off of bones.

Perhaps it was more like a giant stork, wading in shallow water catching fish, frogs and other small animals. Like many pterosaurs *Quetzalcoatlus* bore a head crest, that was probably used in display.

ID FACT FILE

LENGTH:
35 cm (14 in)

TIME:
Early Cretaceous

CLASSIFICATION:
Synapsida
Therapsida
Mammaliaformes
Mammalia
Monotremata

DESCRIPTION:
Medium sized
mammal. Head
probably with
short fleshy bill
and simple
external ears.
Posture probably
sprawling. Hind
foot probably
with sharp spur.

DIET:
Carnivorous,
aquatic
invertebrates.

Steropodon

(lightening tooth)

Steropodon caused a sensation when it
was found in the 1980s. It provided the
first unequivocal evidence that mammals
inhabited Australia during the Mesozoic
Era. Adding to its special status was the
nature of the fossil: it was a jaw with
teeth that had been completely replaced
by opal.

The modern Australian mammal fauna is
dominated by marsupials (pouched

☐ Triassic
248–206 million yrs.

■ Jurassic
206–144 million yrs.

■ Cretaceous
144–65 million yrs.

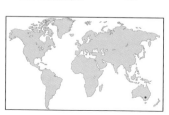

FAMILY ORNITHORHYNCHIDAE (MONOTREMATA)

mammals) so everyone was expecting Australian Mesozoic mammals to have been marsupials as well. However *Steropodon* turned out to be a monotreme closely related to the modern platypus.

Monotremes are an ancient lineage of mammals that lay eggs instead of giving birth to live young. Many more monotremes now have been found in the Mesozoic of Australia, but no marsupials. We now think that marsupials are more recent invaders into Australia that have pushed the monotremes to the very brink of extinction (only three specialized species survive).

FAMILY STAGODONTIDAE (MARSUPALIA)

ID FACT FILE

LENGTH:
50 cm (20 in)

TIME:
Late Cretaceous

CLASSIFICATION:
Synapsida
Therapsida
Mammaliaformes
Mammalia
Marsupalia

DESCRIPTION:
Medium sized
mammal. Body
unknown but
probably four-
legged. Head
probably large
with flesh lobes
surrounding
external ear.
Canine teeth
large. Fingers and
toes probably five.

DIET:
mostly meat,
either from small
animals or from
scavenging.

Didelphodon
(opossum tooth)

Although it is easy to think of Australia as being the home of the marsupials, the marsupials are, in fact, relatively recent invaders of that continent. Indeed they may not have reached it until after the Mesozoic Era had finished.

In contrast North America has a long fossil record of Mesozoic marsupials stretching back to the beginnings of the group. Indeed North America is probably the continent on which marsupials originated.

Triassic
248–206 million yrs.

Jurassic
206–144 million yrs.

Cretaceous
144–65 million yrs.

FAMILY STAGODONTIDAE (MARSUPALIA)

Didelphodon was the largest of these North American Mesozoic marsupials. Its teeth were more adapted to shearing than its opossum relatives, which tend to be omnivorous. This shearing ability would have helped *Didelphodon* cope with a high meat diet. It may have hunted small animals, scavenged dinosaur carcasses or both. Like most primitive mammals it is most likely that *Didelphodon* was nocturnal.

WHAT NEXT?

If after reading this book you feel you would like to know more about the animals described, there are several ways of following up this interest. You can read more about them (see Further Reading pp.10–11), look up one of the many websites on the Internet, visit a museum, or you can join an organisation devoted to their study.

Websites
There are many websites dealing with dinosaurs, of widely varying quality. Here is a short list of some of the better ones.

The Dinosaur
http://www.ucmp.berkeley.edu/diapsids/dinosaur.html
This is a good introductory page.

Zoom Dinosaurs
http://www.EnchantedLearning.com/subjects/dinosaurs
A good introduction to dinosaurs for children.

Dinosaurs On Line
http://www.dinosauria.com
This page is a good repository of lots of dinosaurian information.

There are several catalogues and databases of dinosaurs. These are three of the best and contain exhaustive lists of known dinosaur genera.

The Dinosauricon
http://www.dinosauricon.com

Dinobase
http://www.palaeo.gly.bris.ac.uk/dinobase/dinopage.html

Dinodata http://www.dinodata.net

For information on any dinosaurian topic you can search the archives of the dinosaur mailing list at:

http://www.cmnh.org/fun/dinosaur-archive/index.html which is a discussion group with contributors that include interested amateurs and professional palaeontologists. This archive will also contain instructions on how to subscribe to this list if you wish to do so.

Other good vertebrate palaeontology sites not directly involved with dinosaurs include the following:

Oceans of Kansas
http://www.oceansofkansas.com
An excellent site covering the varied creatures that lived in and around the seas of the Cretaceous.

The Ichthyosaur Pages
http://www.ucmp.berkeley.edu/people/montani/ichthyo/index.html
A good site with lots of detailed information on the 'fish lizards'.

Museums
The Natural History Museum, Cromwell Road, London

National Museum of Wales, Cathays Park, Cardiff

Royal Scottish Museum, Chambers Street, Edinburgh

National Museum of Ireland, Dublin

The Smithsonian Institution, Constitution Avenue, Washington D.C.

American Museum of Natural History, New York

INDEX OF DINOSAURS

INDEX OF ERAS